Maxwell's Demons

Experiments on
Electricity, Magnetism, Light and Modern Physics

Sixth Edition

Brian Jones

Colorado State University
Fort Collins, Colorado

OUTERNET (OP) PUBLISHING

President   Jon K. Earl
Managing Editor   Jennifer Wreisner
Senior Editor   Peggy Li
Executive Editor   Jon Hughes Fuller
Acquisitions Editor   Jeff Davies
Cover Designer   Leslie Anderson

This work was produced by the author(s) and was not subject to editorial review. The author(s) are responsible for accuracy, editing, and content selection.

ISBN 1-58175-509-0

© Cover photo by LAWRENCE BERKELEY LABORATORY / SCIENCE PHOTO LIBRARY.

Demonstration of magnetic levitation using one of the new high-temperature ceramic superconductors. Discovered in 1986, the new superconducting ceramics are expected to lead to a technological revolution & are the subject of intensive worldwide research. Superconductors lose all of their electrical resistance when cooled below a certain threshold temperature. The photograph shows a metal triangle supporting three small magnets floating freely above a nitrogen- cooled bed of numerous pellets of the superconducting ceramic.

Published by Outernet Publishing, LLC
       6595 Edenvale Boulevard, Suite 155
       Eden Prairie, MN 55346
       800-848-2707
       www.outernetpublishing.com

Printed in the United States of America.
10 9 8 7 6 5 4 3 2 1

Contents

Introductory Material

The Experiments

PREFACE

"All mathematical sciences are founded on relations between physical laws and laws of numbers, so that the aim of exact science is to reduce the problems of nature to the determination of quantities by operations with numbers."

- James Clerk Maxwell, *On Faraday's Lines of Force*

By now, having completed one semester of physics, you have figured this out: physics is about this kind of reductionism. Maxwell, of the famous Maxwell equations, did this for electricity and magnetism just as surely as his forebear Newton did for mechanics and dynamics. But Maxwell's work was based on that of Faraday and others - experimental measurements, in the lab. Physics is an empirical science; its equations are intended to describe nature, not to direct it. Physical intuition and insight must be the cornerstone of your knowledge. This lab will provide you with invaluable experience as to how the world works, and how these workings are described in mathematical terms. If you can understand everything that you do in the lab, you will find the rest of the course quite straightforward.

This manual will serve as a guide to the experiments that you will be performing in the Physics 122 or 142 Laboratory. It is not intended as a complete guide; most of the necessary theory is covered in your class and in the textbook, and is not duplicated here. It is also not intended as a cookbook. You will not come into the lab, read recipes and follow formulas. The experiments are more open-ended than this; the experiments are intended to be just that: experiments, and you are encouraged to try different things with the materials that you have. This lab manual will serve as a handy reference and a guide.

The scheduling, exact grading criteria, and other practical matters having to do with lab will be discussed in a separate handout. These and other details will be discussed during your first lab session, which will be a basic introduction to the lab course and some of the techniques that you will be using. Note: the experiments will not be done in the exact order presented in this manual!

We hope you find the manual, and the lab course, to be a valuable and enjoyable part of your physics education. This manual is really a very personal document; it illustrates my views of what is important and interesting in physics. There is a lot of noncritical material in each section that is intended to put things in context: humor, history, philosophy. As I look over the manual each year and make changes, I am occasionally somewhat horrified by what I put in the manual in past years. But some of the tidbits are things I had forgotten; it is nice to encounter them again. I, like most of my colleagues, find physics to be a fascinating subject, and I hope that you too find some wonder in the midst of problems and exams. The lab is a good place for this: you can set things up and see what happens, and if you think about it what you see may surprise you. Don't lose sight of the big picture!

The 6th Edition of Maxwell's Demons has several changes from past versions. Mechanics Review is revised significantly; Quantum Mechanics is brand spanking new. Electric Fields is juiced up. Several experiments have been tarted up here and there - little tweaks to make them work better. And every single document has been worked through to eliminate typos and little errors.

This version owes a great debt to Adam Beehler, who has done some very careful proofreading of previous version. He is a grammar and punctuation maven, and he has been a big help. He also has kept me honest on physics issues, and has been a pleasure to work with. Adam does most of the heavy lifting in terms of keeping the labs running, and he is a constant source of inspiration and new ideas. He is also an excellent teacher, and all around good guy.

Thanks are due to several other people who have helped shape this lab course over the years; I would especially like to thank Jim Sites, Steve Robinson, Marv Heller, Phil Kearney, Bill Fairbank, Siu Au Lee, Bob Leisure, Carl Patton, Bob Wilson, Richard Eykholt, Marty Gelfand, John Harton, Bobby Bracewell, and the many graduate and undergraduate students who have offered constructive criticisms. In 1996-1997, I especially benefitted from the thorough review of the lab by Stuart Deitrick, and a year working with Tim Haywood. Tim has made several substantial upgrades to equipment and has given many good suggestions for new and better ways to do things.

I would also like to thank my wife Carol for being my partner in all of life's adventures. Much of who I am is due to her wonderful influence.

By the way: Maxwell's Demon is a *gedanken* concept used in discussing the Second Law of Thermodynamics. It is the same Maxwell as above. The Demon is a being who sorts atoms by their temperature—for reasons I can explain if you'd like me to. Or you could just read *The Crying of Lot 49 by Thomas Pynchon*.

Go in peace.

Brian Jones
Ft. Collins, Colorado
June, 2004

"And furthermore, my son, be admonished: of making many books
there is no end; and much study is a weariness of the flesh."

- Ecclesiastes 12:12

Introduction

Philosophy

"Aristotle maintained that women have fewer teeth than men; although he was twice married, it never occurred to him to verify this statement by examining his wives' mouths."

- Bertrand Russell, in *The Impact of Science on Society*

Science is not a collection of facts, or a collection of theories. Science is a process, a method; at its core is observation. Everything in your physics course that you will learn is based on measurements that someone, somewhere has made. Aristotle felt that such empirical work was not the proper way to ascertain the truth; he felt that this could only be arrived at by reflection. He had good reasons to believe that women had fewer teeth than men, so he saw no reason to check to see whether or not they actually did.

Nowadays people generally understand the importance of measurement to science. This is the basic reason for having you do a lab course as part of your physics training: physics is an empirical science, and in order to really understand what it is about, it is crucial that you actually get into the lab and make some measurements. If you will go on in science, the principles of experimentation that you learn in the lab will be very important. It is simply not possible to be a good scientist without having a good understanding of how to do an experiment.

"I often say that when you can measure what you are speaking about, and express it in numbers, you know something about it; but when you cannot measure it, when you cannot express it in numbers, your knowledge is of a mean and unsatisfactory kind."

- William Thompson (Lord Kelvin)

There is, of course, an additional reason for having the laboratory be an integral part of your first physics course. By using the equipment and making measurements in the lab, you will gain an increased understanding and appreciation of the concepts that you will be learning in class and applying on homework problems. In all of the experiments that you will be doing, the central point, the crux of the biscuit as it were, is for you to better understand the phenomena being explored. There are some practical consequences of this philosophy. For one, the experiments are not designed to be "finished"; you should keep working until the end of the period. And the experiments are open-ended; *you* will decide, with your lab partners, what measurements to make, and how.

Puzzles

We have discussed why we feel you should do experimental work when learning science, but this does not explain why you might *want* to do this. There must be more to it.

And, in fact, there is. Science is really about solv-

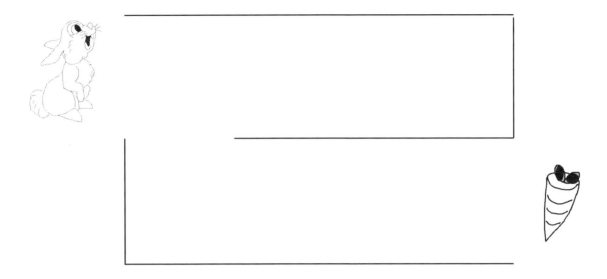

Help Mr. Bun make his way to the yummy carrot!

Figure 1: Example of puzzle typical of glossy children's magazine found in dentists' offices. Can you solve it? (Hint: the bunny can't go through walls.)

Figure 2: More advanced puzzle behavior typical of average CSU student. These and other questions are best talked about over a cappucino at Déjà Vu Coffeehouse.

ing puzzles. When you were younger, you perhaps had magazines in your house that had puzzles in them like the one in Figure 1. (Go ahead and try to solve it, if you wish.) Kids like solving puzzles; generally, young children, when science is presented to them in an engaging fashion, love it. They love doing experiments, making observations—because they like solving puzzles.

As we get older, we still enjoy a good puzzle; they just get a bit more complex, as in Figure 2. But the spirit is still there. When you have posed a good question, it can be very satisfying to be able to find the answer—and this is where experiment comes in. If you wonder, say, whether women have fewer teeth than men, you can make a measurement! In this lab, you will be presented with physical situations, and you will be given tools. You will use the tools to make measurements, and from these measurements you will make conclusions—you will basically be solving puzzles.

In fact, to help you keep this in mind, we will regularly present exercises in the lab as puzzles. You might see a section like this:

PUZZLE

You have been given a ball launcher and a marble that can be shot from it. You may make one firing of the ball launcher—straight up. You may not fire it at an angle. Given the measurements you make on this one test firing, you should calculate at what angle the launcher needs to be set in order to launch a ball so that it lands in the box.

This is a puzzle, and you are expected to solve it not with trial and error—just shooting over and over again until you get it right—but by using the physics you have learned to make calculations.

Predictions

Scholars of science often say that science proceeds by what is known, appropriately, as the scientific method: you make a hypothesis, predict the outcome of an experiment based on this hypothesis, perform the experiment, and then analyze what

happened. Was your prediction correct? If not, how can you alter your hypothesis to suit the new data?

In fact, this aspect of science is overemphasized. Often, great discoveries come from people just trying things out to see what happens. But there is no doubt that the method is powerful—particularly if you are attacking a very thorny, complex problem.

"The real purpose of scientific method is to make sure Nature hasn't misled you into thinking you know something you don't actually know.... That's the main reason why so much scientific and mechanical information sounds so dull and so cautious. If you get careless or go romanticizing scientific information, giving it a flourish here and there, Nature will soon make a complete fool of you."

- Robert Pirsig, *Zen and the Art of Motorcycle Maintenance*

In this lab, you will be working to develop your models of how the world works. To do this most effectively, you will need to use the scientific method: to make predictions, and then test them. You will often see sections in the lab manual that explicitly ask you to make a prediction:

PREDICTION

Before making any measurements, talk to the other members of your group and decide what you think will happen. Sketch what you think the velocity vs. time graph will look like.

It is *crucial* that you in fact work this way. If you just do the measurements and say, "Oh yeah—that's what I thought it would look like," you are cheating yourself. Anyone can say what will happen after it already has. It is the mark of a scholar to predict what will happen before it does.

Pluginski

This is a term that is used to describe the means that many physics students use to solve problems:

plugging into a formula. The problem is that this is algebra. What we want you to learn is problem solving.

I had a friend who took a physics course in which the students were asked to estimate and calculate a number of different things that, on the surface, had nothing to do with physics. For instance, they were asked to estimate how many piano tuners there were in New York City. The point was to get students used to solving problems for which no formulas exist. Then, when they had to solve physics problems, they would first think about what was happening physically before ever putting pen to paper.

In the lab, much of what you do will be qualitative. Work toward an understanding of what is happening, and what the terms mean. What is acceleration? What is force? What was the ball doing at this point on the graph? Worry less about numbers, and more about a physical model of what is happening.

Positive Attitude

It is not doing the thing we like to do, but liking the thing we have to do, that makes life blessed.

- Goethe

You are going to be spending two hours each week in the lab; that is a given. You can't pass the course without taking the lab. You might as well work carefully, work hard, and learn something. And you might as well have fun doing it. As you will surmise from this manual, we intend that you should enjoy lab.

Good luck with the lab and the rest of the course. Please let me know if there is any way that this manual, or any part of the lab course, might be improved.

How to Do a Lab

Preparing Ahead

The information contained in this lab manual will serve as your guide to understanding and performing the experiments that you will be doing. The description of each experiment will generally consist of the following sections:

> Opening Remarks
> Necessary Theory
> Experiments and Calculations
> Summing Up

You should read all of this material before coming to lab. You will sometimes find that there are calculations that you are asked to do *before* coming to lab; these will generally be discussed in the Necessary Theory section. The lab manual is not intended to be a stand-alone source. When reading through it, you will want to refer to your text and your notes.

Though an attempt is made to have the labs follow the lectures so that you are doing a lab shortly after you have discussed the phenomenon in class, this is not always possible. The emphasis in the lab portion of the course is different, and equipment must be shared by different labs. So you may well find that you are doing an experiment on a topic that has not yet been discussed in lecture. Some people actually prefer this; they find that the hands-on experience prepares them well for the coverage of the topic in lecture and problems. Either way, the lab and the rest of the course are meant to complement each other; both are important to your understanding.

Great works are performed, not by strength, but by perseverance.

- Samuel Johnson

First Two Minutes of Lab

The first two minutes or so of lab will be used by your instructor to describe the equipment for the day's lab, tips on how to use it, and briefly outline what measurements and calculations you are expected to make. Pay particular attention to the practical details of how the equipment works. Your instructor will be speaking to you as if you have read the lab manual, as it is assumed that you have.

The Rest of the Lab

The description of the rest of the lab period takes the form of a dialogue between a student and a lab instructor.

Student: Tell me, O wise one, how will I know when I have finished the lab and can go?

Instructor: The authorities in the university have set times for the beginning and ending of classes. As it is for a lecture, so it is for a lab; when the appointed hour for the start of lab arrives, the lab begins; when the hour for the end of lab arrives you are free to go.

Student: Why may we not leave when we have finished the experiment?

Instructor: As an author knows well, to the writing of books there is no end. So it is in lab; there will always be other measurements to make, other calculations to perform. You will not reach a place where you can truly say that you have done all that can be done. Therefore you must do what you can in the short time that you have.

Student: How will I know whether what I have done is sufficient?

Instructor: If you work carefully and steadily for the period of the lab, the work that you have produced will be sufficient. For the real value of your work is not in what you have produced, but in what you have learned. You will have gained an understanding, and will go away fulfilled. You need not do every part of every lab; in fact, you will not be able to.

Student: Does that mean I will never get a +?

Instructor: Worry less about grades, and more about what you have learned. A grade should be a reflection of what you have learned; work well, and you shall be rewarded.

Student: I will not be able to do all of the experiments; how do I know which to do? And what if I have another idea?

Instructor: It is truly part of the enterprise of science to know not where your investigations will lead. Begin as instructed; make further inquiries as you deem best. You, with your lab partners, must best decide how to proceed. What will help your understanding most? What will be most interesting? Some approaches are better than others, but there is truly no right or wrong.

Student: Then how are grades assigned?

Instructor: Grades, my friend, are at best a necessary evil. This is why we have limited the evil to three forms: +, √ and -. Your lab instructor will assign grades based on your performance. Most people will receive the grade of "√"; a select few who have done noteworthy work will receive a "+" grade. In the rare cases where a student has not performed adequately, a "-" may be given. The grading system is loose; it recognizes achievement, but it was devised in the realization that grading the labs is not easy, and so a system with more grades was not helpful.

Student: Thank you, O sage and honest one. Do you have any last advice for me?

Instructor: I do. Our goal for you in the lab is for you to better understand the concepts of physics, appreciate the nature of experimentation, and sense the enjoyment that comes from open-ended exploration.

Working in Groups

When you eventually seek gainful employment in the "real world", you will find that you have to work with others. Most of what you will be doing will be in cooperation with others doing the same or different jobs. In the lab, this is crucial: working with a group, you can bounce ideas off your lab partners, and one of you might have an insight that he or she can share. You will find that you can do more work more effectively in a group that works well together.

All of the experiments that you will do in this section of the course will be done in groups. As you will work in groups, the report that you submit on the experiment will also be a group report; the grade that you receive on the lab will be a group grade. The goal in this case is to cooperate, and, working together, to produce a better effort than you could individually. It is important to find a group that you can work comfortably with.

One difficulty to watch out for: you should rotate responsibilities in your group. If one person is always the "secretary", recording data and writing comments, he or she will not get the best possible experience in the lab. You should see to it that each report that your group submits has parts that were written by each of you, and has work that was done by each of you. The goal of the lab is understanding; it is more important that each person understand exactly what is being done than that the report that you turn in is the "best" in some sense.

One final note: as some of the lab grade is based on what is done in lab, if you are not a full participant in the experiment, you may find that your grade is lower than that of the rest of the group. This departure from the group grade is only made in these cases, in which one person is not fully taking part.

The Lab Write-Up

Your instructor will speak to you often as the lab goes on. Nonetheless, a fair amount of his or her idea about what your group has done in lab will be formed as a result of the written record of your work: the lab write-up.

The lab write-up should be a complete record of what you did in lab, produced as you work. One person in your group should be at all times chronicling what you are doing: what data you are taking, and why; what conclusions you draw from your data, and why. At the end of lab your group will submit this report to your instructor; don't forget that what you are writing is to be read by another person! A major part of any scientific enterprise is communicating what you have done; you should take care that your write-up is as good as the work you did in lab! Use the proper number of significant figures, record results in tables, record details of what you have done. There is no fixed style, but there are elements that should be present. Use your common sense; your instructor will also provide useful guidance.

Grading

The things that you will learn in lab are not so easy to grade you on; therefore the lab grading system is a very loose one. During each lab your instructor will observe your progress with the experiment as you record your data, calculations and conclusions. At the end of lab your group will submit a report to the instructor in charge of the lab. Based on

an assessment of your performance in lab and on what you have recorded in your notebook your instructor will give you a grade on the lab. Your performance in lab counts; you will not be graded only on what is in your report. It is important that you be a full participant in each experiment. The grade that your group will receive on the lab will be one of the following:

+	Outstanding effort
√	Good effort
-	Weak effort; significant defects
0	Lab missed

Most groups will get a "√" grade on most labs. This means that you are making good progress. At the end of the term, your lab grades will be included with your course grade in a manner that will be outlined by the professor in charge of the course.

Occasionally students worry that their grade will suffer because they have a "hard" instructor. This is generally not a problem. Most of the lab instructors grade about the same, and the grading system is so loose that there is very little difference between sections and between students. But, at the end of the semester, should significant differences in grading exist, care will be taken to adjust the grades for the different sections so that they are similar.

One final note on grading: if you behave conscientiously in lab, you will get marks that reflect it; a "-" grade usually indicates carelessness, laziness or both. Do not worry about your grades; concentrate on doing a good job, and the good grades will follow.

Lab Behavior

The lab is part of a normal academic course, and should be treated as such. You should be on time, be prepared for what you will be doing, and work conscientiously. The person in charge of the lab is your instructor; you should accord him or her the same respect that you would accord any course instructor. Overall responsibility for course grading and attendance rests with the professor in charge of the course.

We do several labs a day in the same room with the same equipment. Thus it is important that you leave the equipment as you found it! I cannot stress the importance of this too much. Turn equipment off, return any bits that you have borrowed from other tables, and generally straighten up before you leave lab. It is also important that you do not alter anything on the computers; you can change anything you want, **but do not save your changes!!** This will be stressed again and again.

At times we will be working with equipment that will require safety precautions. Please be attentive to them. We use no equipment that is not absolutely safe if used properly, but we will use some equipment that must be used properly to be used safely.

Please treat the equipment with care; if you are unsure as to how to use a piece of equipment, ask! Your instructor is familiar with the working of each piece of equipment in the lab and can answer your questions. Asking early will keep you from damaging equipment or wasting time.

Missed Labs

The laboratory is a required part of your physics course. Attendance at all weekly sessions of your assigned lab is required, as is completion of all lab write-ups. There are serious penalties for missing labs.

We do understand, though, that there may be circumstances in which you may have to be absent for a lab session. In this case, it is your responsibility to make up the lab in another section. For instance, if your lab is held Tuesday from 10 -12, and you are ill at that time, you can go to the session Thursday at the same time to make it up. The course schedule will have a list of when sections are offered; note that sections may be cancelled. When you make up the lab in another section, you should complete the write-up in lab as usual. You will hand in your report to the supervising instructor. You must also fill out a grade transfer request form (available in lab) so that the instructor grading the report from your group will know where to send your grade so that you get proper credit for it.

If you miss a lab for a good reason and are unable to make it up you may request an excused absence. This can only be granted by the professor in charge of the course. Please note that *it is not possible to make up a lab after the week of the lab has passed.* Keep this in mind; if you have an unexcused absence from lab, there is no way to make it up after the week in which the absence occurred.

Questions, Problems and Comments

If you have a problem, complaint, question or suggestion about lab, please communicate it. Your lab instructor is a good first person to turn to. More general comments about the course may be directed to the professor in charge of the course. Requests for scheduling changes should be directed to Steve Robinson (office in D105, Engineering Building). Specific comments about the lab and the manual may be referred to Brian Jones, the lab coordinator (office in Engineering 209).

The labs are continually being revised; any comment you have about the labs would be very useful - please pass your ideas on!

The Experiments...

"What is the use of a book," thought Alice, "without pictures or conversations?"

- Lewis Carroll, *Alice's Adventures in Wonderland*

Mechanics Review

Motion, forces, energy, and all that stuff from last semester

Opening Remarks

"For years now, most automobiles have been designed to roughly resemble eggs. Manufacturers claim the ovoid shape maximizes aerodynamic efficiency, but if that is true, how come a bird has to break out of the egg before it can fly?"

Tom Robbins, Half Asleep in Frog Pajamas

Last semester, you had occasion to learn about some of the most basic concepts in physics: motion, forces, energy, heat - and how we use these basic concepts to solve problems. You may have noted that the first semester of physics is a required prerequisite to take this second semester course. You really need to know and understand all of that stuff before going on in this course.

This lab is a bit of a chance to review all the material that you learned previously, to reacquaint yourself with it. Welcome back! Now, let's get down to work.

Theory

The theory for this lab, we will assume, is, by this point in your academic career, deeply engraved on your conciousness. It's all that stuff you learned in the first semester course.

Experiments and Calculations

Necessary Equipment

This lab will be set up as experiment stations: there will be several different experiment stations around the room, and you will go from table to table working on different experiments. The experiments are, really, the greatest hits from the first semester: the key concepts and lab techniques that we want to be certain you recall.

Pick a group to work with, and go from station to station trying out the different experiments that are detailed below. Your lab instructor will give you some advice about where to focus your energies, as well as how much you will be expected to complete.

The Experiments

You can read about the different experiments that are set up at the stations for this lab in the following pages.

Figure 1: Jumbo's prodigious memory (he never forgot a formula) would have made him a great physics student, but his fear of the mouse kept him from being able to use the computer effectively.

MECHANICS REVIEW

Hot Wheels Physics: Loop-the-Loop

Loop-the-Loop

Now look at the track arrangement shown below. The car will roll down the ramp, and, if it is going fast enough, navigate the loop-the-loop. If you sent the car down the ramp with the minimum speed possible, it should just barely be touching the track at the top of the loop; any slower, and it would leave the track at this point. You should know enough physics to predict how fast the car needs to be going at this point, and, therefore, how high up the ramp it needs to start in order to just make the loop.

You can make as many measurements on the car and the track as you would like. Your job is to predict, for a track set up as in the picture, how high up the track to start the car in order to have it *just* make it around the loop. You will need to say something about friction. You might have additional complications; maybe your car's bumper will scrape when it goes around the loop.

PREDICTION

Make whatever measurements you need to, then predict where the care needs to be set in order to just make it around the loop. Set the car at the correct height, let it go, and watch what happens.

Does the car go around the loop as expected? If it does, test this: try the car a little bit farther down the track, and then let it go. If you were correct, the car should leave the track this time. Can you tell? If the car did not make it around the loop, can you see anywhere you might have gone wrong?

MECHANICS REVIEW

Hot Wheels Physics: Death-Defying Jump

Death-Defying Jump

Suppose you have a car follow the track arrangement shown below. The car will roll down the track, fly off the end, and land on the floor. At this point, you should know enough physics to predict where the car will land, given where it started from on the ramp. In fact, that is just what you will be asked to do.

You can make as many measurements on the car and the track as you would like. Your job is to predict, for a track set up as below and for a given starting height, where to put the cup to catch the car.

The basic technique is pretty easy to guess: use conservation of energy to predict how fast the car will be moving when it leaves the table. But there are the real-world factors to consider too.

Can you think of a way to work friction in? You can make simple measurements on the car and the track—in fact, you will need to—but you can't make a trial jump!

PREDICTION

Make whatever measurements you need to, then predict where the cup needs to be. Set the cup at the correct point, set the car at the determined height, and give it a shot.

Does the car land where you expect it to? If not, can you see anywhere you might have gone wrong?

Muscles and Bones: Center of Mass

Description

People of different body shape have different positions of their centers of mass. In particular, men and women tend to have very different center of mass positions: women tend to have a lower center of mass than men. In this exercise you will get the chance to determine the position of the center of mass of one or more members of your group by direct measurement.

Equipment

• Person to make measurements on
• Center of mass measurement system (long board with support at one end, scale at the other)

Experiments

1) Pick two subjects for the experiment. Ideally, you will be able to choose two subjects with different body shapes.

2) Measure the masses of the two subjects by using the bathroom scale.

3) Now set up the board system, with one end of the board on the scale and one end on the support. Note the weight recorded on the scale; this is the contribution from the board itself, and is to be subtracted of.

4) Now have a subject lie down on the board, with the bottom of their feet right at the edge of the support. Measure the weight recorded on the scale and the length of the board from this point to the scale. Draw a force and torque diagram of this situation. Given the date you have, calculate the position of the person's center of mass as a distance from the bottom of their feet. How does this point fall with respect to their hips? What is the ratio of the height of their center of mass to their height?

5) Now repeat the measurement for your second subject. How does their center of mass fall with respect to their hips?

6) Compare what you have observed for the two subjects. Can you make any general conclusions?

7) You might want to try one of the center of mass exercises noted in your text.

Muscles and Bones: The Curl

Description

A curl is a weight lifting move in which a weight is lifted by the forearm alone. The maximum weight that can be lifted this way is a function of the angle that the forearm makes with the upper arm.

Equipment

• Person to make measurements on
• Dumbbells with range of masses
• Protractor to measure angles

Experiments

1) Pick a subject for the experiment - someone of average strength.

2) Have the subject stand or sit next to a table or bench with his or her forearm horizontal on the table. By adjusting his or her upper arm, the subject should be able to change the angle between his or her upper arm and forearm.

3) Record the maximum mass of dumbbell that the subject can lift for different starting angles between forearm and upper arm. Try a broad range: at the very least do 90, 135° and 180°.

4) Explain, using a diagram, the differences in the maximum mass the subject can lift for the different angles. Why does the angle make a difference?

MECHANICS REVIEW

Fluids: Blood Pressure

In this section of the lab you will be using an automated blood pressure measurement device. **Please don't run the device with no finger (or wrist) in the cuff. This can damage it.**

This measurement is going to take some time and patience for the guinea pig in your group—the person on whom you will make measurements. Have the g.p. (as the person will be affectionately known for the rest of the lab) get comfy on a stool and set his or her arm on the lab bench, roughly at the height of their heart.

Next, measure the blood pressure in the g.p.'s finger; record the numbers for the systolic and diastolic pressure (which one is higher?) These numbers are given in mm of Hg.

After you have made a measurement on the g.p., you will need to wait 5-10 minutes before another reading can be made—cutting off blood flow into the finger, as the cuff does, changes things a bit. You need to wait until things are back to normal again. Have the g.p. sit tight and not get excited so that their blood pressure stays constant.

Use a meter stick to make a measurement: if the g.p. puts their arm up in the air over their head, how much higher will their finger be than it was when you took the first measurement?

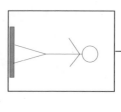

🖙 PREDICTION 🖙

Given this, predict: how high will the blood pressure in the g.p.'s finger be when it is in this position? Assume that the g.p.'s blood vessels form a continuous column, and so you can use Pascal's principle and the other pressure rules you have learned. (Note: you will need to do some unit conversions. The formulas that you have learned are in the mks units of Pascals; the device measures in mm of Hg.)

Once you have made a prediction, test it out. Have the g.p. hold their arm up, and measure. Does the pressure change by about the amount you predicted? Keep in mind that blood pressure can vary a bit even over short times, and that the device is not totally accurate.

? QUESTION ?

If the g.p. will stand for it, let them recover a bit and then measure the blood pressure with their hand held down. Predict what the pressure should be, and then test.

? QUESTION ?

Are you surprised at how low the pressure goes in this case? How high would the g.p. need to raise their hand so that the diastolic blood pressure in the hand would go to zero? Are there people with arms this long?

? QUESTION ?

Now, a first aid tip: suppose you cut your finger, and it's bleeding fast enough that it's giving you a case of the fantods. Can you think of a good, quick strategy to slow the bleeding down? Explain what to do, and why it works.

? QUESTION ?

If someone is feeling lightheaded, why do you have them lie down? (Well, there are really two reasons: one is that if are standing up and faint, they might injure themselves in a fall, but if they are lying down and they faint, they won't. We are looking for another reason here.) Lying down can actually solve the problem of the lightheadedness; why?

MECHANICS REVIEW

Newton's Laws: Otis Elevator's Rapid Weight Loss Plan

Take the bathroom scale provided, and set it on the floor of an elevator in the building. (You have your choice of two; your instructor can provide locations.) Start on the top floor of the building.

Next, press the button for the basement. As the elevator moves, note any changes in your weight as recorded by the scale. Sketch a graph for how your weight varied, and note the maximum and minimum values.

Finally, explain (using a free-body diagram) why the numbers recorded on the scale changed. Can you estimate the acceleration of the elevator from the numbers you have?

MECHANICS REVIEW

Newton's Laws: Running Against the Wind

Measure the acceleration of your fan cart (on high speed) on flat ground using the sonic ranger. Measure the mass of the fan cart using a balance.

Now, predict the angle θ at which a board can be set so that the fan cart will be able to just hold itself up, without moving up or down the ramp.

After you have made a prediction, check yourself. Is your prediction confirmed?

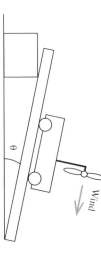

Wind

MECHANICS REVIEW

Physics of Toys: Bottle Rocket

Description

The water rocket is a safe toy that illustrates the principles of rocket propulsion. And it gets you wet while you are using it: what more can you ask from a toy? When you are using the rocket, NEVER PUMP UP THE ROCKET MORE THAN 20 PUMPS!!!

• How high does the rocket go? Is there a simple way that you could measure this? (Hint: think time. We have stopwatches!)

• Is there another way that you could measure the height? (Hint: think trigonometry!)

Physics Principles

Here's the big question: what makes this thing fly? What's the point of the water, besides getting you wet?

Suggestions for Experimentation

• Launch the rocket a few times with different ratios of water and air. What is the best mixture? Just what is the role of the water? The air? Fly the rocket with just water or just air. Does this help you figure this out?

7

Physics of Toys: Yo-yo

Description

This yo-yo is a very special one, designed to "sleep" a very long time. Toss it down, and watch it rest at the end of the string. What do you hear right before it comes up? The string is fixed fast to the hub of the yo-yo, and there is a clutch on the hub that allows it to freely spin as long as the spin rate is above some value. The big question is: how does this baby work?

at the same rotational speed? How could you measure this? If you do make this measurement, you will find that it is another good hint as to how the clutch works!

Physics Principles

There are a few things to answer here:

• What energy changes are taking place when you use the yo-yo? Specifically, when the yo-yo comes back up, where does the energy come from to allow it to do this?

• How does the clutch work? You can get a good hint by looking at the side of the yo-yo to see the inner workings.

Suggestions for Experimentation

• Does the clutch disengage and engage

Mechanics of Sports: Weightlifting

Work and Power in Weightlifting

This is a clip from the 1996 Atlanta Olympics. The frame rate is 30 frames per second, you will need to make an estimate of the height of the weightlifter in order to calibrate the distance. (That will be accurate enough for the measurements you are to make.) In this clip, Andrey Chemerkin does what is known as a "clean and jerk"; he does the "clean" in which he gets the bar up to his chest, and the "jerk" in which he raises it over his head.

1) During the "clean" phase of the lift, how much work does he do? Given how much work he has done, how much power is he putting out? Is this a lot of power?

2) Note that Chemerkin's arms are spread apart a lot on the bar. This makes the bar more stable, but it also means that he uses the muscles in his arms less efficiently - the horizontal components of the forces from his two arms cancel. But this does help him in another way - how does having his arms apart change the energy required during the "jerk" phase of the lift?

3) Can you estimate how much force the weights makes when they hit the ground?

Preview Video Clip   (You can use the control bar to play or re-play the clip. When you are done viewing the clip, click on the close box.)

Weightlifting Movie

Start Analysis Program

Analyze   (When you are done with your analysis, quit the program to return to this screen.)

Back to Start

Summing Up

There are really two points to this lab: to refresh your memory about the material from the first course, but also to give you an introduction to this lab course, to your instructor, and to your fellow students.

The problems, too, might well remind you of what a powerful set of tools you acquired in the first semester. Newton's Laws and the other material of the course - Newton's Toolbox, as it were - are a powerful set of equations and techniques for solving a wide range of problems. It is no big surprise that after the great successes of Newton and his successors, philosophers and scientists took a very mechanistic view of the universe. A good example of this sentiment is from Laplace:

"Given for one instant an intelligence which could comprehend all the forces by which nature is animated and the respective positions of the beings which compose it, if moreover this intelligence were vast enough to submit these data to analysis, it would embrace in the same formula both the movements of the largest bodies in the universe and those of the lightest atom; to it nothing would be uncertain, and the future as the past would be present to its eyes."

This second semester course will introduce you to another set of tools for dealing with electricity and magnetism, and also with light and optics. But at the end of the course, the 20th century physics topics you will learn about will make it clear that things aren't quite so simple. 20th century physics has taught us that physics is not so starkly deterministic as the laws of Newton and Maxwell; God does indeed play dice with the universe. The formulas that you learn will serve you well, but only in limited contexts. As this has become clear, it has given folks a deeper, more complex understanding of our world. And it has shown that there are certain problems that physics is really not a good tool to handle. The rational, reductionist analysis you are taught in science is great for pendulums, but when it comes to love, you're on your own. Not everything in life can be reduced to a formula. The sixth Dalai Lama agreed when he wrote:

"The girl was perhaps born not of a mother,
But blossomed in a peach tree.
Her love fades
Quicker than peach flowers.
Although I know her soft body
I cannot sound out her heart;
Yet we have but to make a few lines on a chart
And the distance to the farthest stars
In the sky can be measured."

Go in peace.

Figure 2: We have various means of motivating people to participate in lab. We can all hope it does not come down to this.

Static Electricity

A Qualitative Investigation

Opening Remarks

"Early to bed, and early to rise, makes a man healthy, wealthy and wise."

- Benjamin Franklin, *Poor Richard's Almanac*

Many of the common aphorisms that we use on a daily basis were penned by Benjamin Franklin in his early years, as part of his *Poor Richard's Almanac*. Of course, he later had a career as a statesman, being one of the founders of the United States and the original signers of the Declaration of Independence. Somewhere along the way, perhaps by following his own advice to be parsimonious with time and resources...

"Dost thou love life? Then do not squander time; for that's the stuff life is made of."

- Benjamin Franklin, *Ibid.*

...he found the time to be a scientist. Many people know the story of the kite and the key, but not many people know that he was one of the first people to make a systematic study of electrostatics. In fact, it is Benjamin Franklin who gave us the conventions of which kind of charge is called "+" and which kind "-", which I and many others have come to rue. (Hey—he didn't know about electrons, so it was a 50-50 chance.) The work that you will be doing today is based on Franklin's work, as modernized by Robert Morse, who has spent a fair amount of time making updated versions of Franklin's equipment using modern, cheap materials.

Necessary Theory

Charges

Gravity, the force that we are most familiar with, is pretty wimpy compared to the forces of electrostatics. But whereas there is only one type of gravitational "charge" (mass) and so all objects attract one another gravitationally, there are two signs of charge: "+" and "-". (There seems to be a correspondence with lab grades, but, sadly, there is no charge of "check.") And, as Ben Franklin discovered, like charges repel and opposites attract. This means that neutral matter—with as many "+" charges as "-"—will not be attracted or repelled from other neutral matter. All of the forces will cancel. Thus, the force that matters most on a daily basis is in fact gravity. (There is one proviso here. Where matter comes into contact with other matter, the electrostatic forces do come into play.) In this lab, you will accumulate excess charges on objects by contact. You will get objects with net charges on them, and you will explore their interactions.

Conductors and Insulators

When you begin to charge up objects, you will find that there are two different kinds of materials, with respect to their behavior concerning charges: conductors and insulators. Charge can flow freely in conductors; it cannot flow in insulators. You can charge up either a conductor or an insulator, but if you charge up a conductor, the charge that you put on it will not stay where you put it!

Figure 1: Benjamin Franklin, apprenticed as he was to a printer (his brother) at the age of 12, no doubt got a chance to try his hand at my first occupation: that of paperboy. This is certainly the job that I have had that I was best at.

Experiments and Observations

Necessary Equipment

The equipment that you will use for this experiment is made from materials that you are probably familiar with: styrofoam plates and cups, string, aluminum pie plates, neon light bulbs, Scotch tape. This lab really uses a lot of technology, but it is technology that you have become accustomed to. Ben Franklin couldn't just cruise out to Wal-Mart and get a 100-pack of styrofoam plates.

Each group will receive an electrophorus (see Figure 2), a basic measurement tool, with the following pieces:

Aluminum plate with styrofoam cup handle and:
    attached neon lamp
    attached foil ball on string
    attached batch of tinsel

Please be careful with the electrophorus, as it is not very sturdy!

You will also receive some basic supplies; please conserve!

    Scotch tape
    Styrofoam pie plates

This is a great piece of equipment, as it uses everyday items like styrofoam cups that have remarkable properties that we normally take for granted.

Charging: Some Fun with Tape

For this experiment, you will use your roll of tape. Proceed as follows:

• Pull one strip of tape (about 10 cm long) off the roll, and stick one end to a fingertip.

When you pull tape off the roll, it will be charged. Generally, folks are taught that you need to rub things together to charge them up; this is not in fact true. What is important is *contact* between two surfaces. Rubbing two surfaces together increases the surface area in contact, but the action of rubbing is not necessary. For tape, where the two surfaces are (by design) in very intimate contact, it is sufficient to pull the tape off the roll. One side of the tape likes electrons more than the other, and it takes more than its share when it goes.

How can you show that the tape is charged? Bring the strip near another finger. What do you observe?

QUESTION

The tape is charged, but your finger is not. Why does the tape attract your finger? Hint: your finger is a conductor, and charges are free to move. Suppose the tape was charged negatively; what will happen to the electrons in your finger? They will tend to be repelled. So the side of your finger nearest the tape will tend to be positively charged, but the opposite side will be negative. How does this make a net force? Is this force always attractive? Sketch a diagram of what is going on between your finger and the tape.

Rules for Charges: Yet More Fun with Tape

Next, proceed as follows:

• Pull a second strip of tape (about 10 cm) off the roll.

QUESTION

What sign of charge should this piece of tape have relative to the first one you pulled off?

PREDICTION

Given this, should the two strips attract each other, or repel?

Make a prediction, and test.

You should find that the two strips are charged up the same way, which makes sense, since they were both pulled from the roll in the same way.

PREDICTION

Is there a way that you can take your two strips and make them acquire opposite charges? If they were oppositely charged,

how could you tell?

Think about this. A hint: if you take two strips of tape, and put them together (sticky side of one to the smooth side of the other) you can take most of the charge off the pair by gently sliding your fingers along the sides of the tape. Now what happens when you pull them apart....

Come up with a procedure for making two oppositely charged strips of tape, and predict:

PREDICTION

How will the two strips behave toward each other? Will they attract or repel?

Make a prediction, and test. This one can be tricky! There can be some unexpected results. Give some thoughts as to what might be happening if you discover something you don't expect.

Now, one final question: how could you tell whether the tape is charged negatively or positively? Ultimately, you will want to measure this. In order to do so, you will need to be able to make more careful measurements, to which end we present...

The Electrophorus

Your electrophorus will appear as in Figure 2: a styrofoam cup attached to an aluminum plate, with various "instrumentation" around the sides. You will put charge on your electrophorus as follows:

• Charge up a styrofoam plate by rubbing it on the table or the carpet. How can you tell if it is charged or not? (Note: if you just can't get any charge this way, you can get a good charge off the computer monitor.)

• Next, set the plate upside-down on your desk. Bring the electrophorus down to it (note: you should hold the electrophorus by the cup, an insulating handle, so that the charge does not bleed off through you!), and rub it against the plate to pull charge off it.

Is your electrophorus charged? If it is, you should be able to tell by looking at the tinsel bunch.

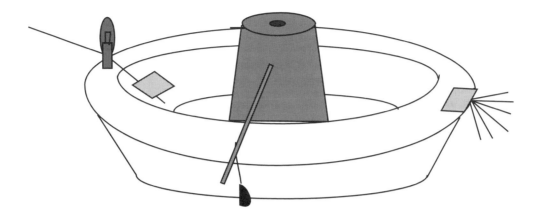

Figure 2: The electrophorus, as updated by Robert Morse. Though it seems simple, in fact it is made of a collection of very high-tech materials. It is certainly far superior to what Benjamin Franklin had to work with!

QUESTION

How does the tinsel bunch allow you to tell whether or not your electrophorus is charged or not? Explain this in some detail.

You may find that it is hard to get charge on your electrophorus this way. If so, there is a second technique that you can try. Even if you can charge it up the first way, try the second way to see which is more effective.

The Electrophorus: Charging by Induction

Charge up your plate as before, and set it upside down on the desk. Next, proceed as follows:

• Bring the electrophorus (again, holding it by the cup) near to the plate, *but do not let the two touch!* You should see that the tinsel bunch reacts; this means that the plate is charged.

• Next, keep the electrophorus where it is, and touch the side of the aluminum plate with your finger. You should feel a small spark; charge is being transferred! Notice what happens to the tinsel bunch when you do this.

• Finally, pull the electrophorus away. What happens to the tinsel bunch now?

What you have just done is to charge the electrophorus by induction. You did not transfer any charge from the plate to the electrophorus; to see that this is true, discharge the plate to your finger, and start over. You can keep charging the electrophorus up this way indefinitely! The charge on the plate is not used up.

This brings up the logical question: where does the charge come from? And, in true constructivist spirit, this is a question that you, not I, will answer.

QUESTION

How does this process get a charge on the electrophorus? Draw a sketch to show what is happening with the charge at each stage.

Remember that the plate is a conductor, and charges are free to move!

Now you have seen two different ways to charge up the electrophorus. Which is more effective? This is the technique you should use. Once you have your electrophorus charged up, we can do some other exercises with it.

The Connection with Current Electricity

In days of old, there were two different kinds of electricity that people dealt with: static electricity, and current electricity. Static electricity could make things stick together or repel, and current electricity, which at the time came from batteries, used a flow of current to do useful work. Now we recognize that these are one and the same; if the charge from the electrophorus moves off it, this is a current, and it can do some useful work on the way.

Well, not really useful in the way that you might think of it, but it is useful work in the physicist's sense. Try this: charge up your electrophorus, and then bring your finger near (but not touching) the little foil ball suspended from the stick through the handle. The ball should start bouncing back and forth. How does the rate of bouncing change as time goes on? The obvious thing to do is to ask, "Hey—what's going on?" And, since this is a constructivist lab, you know what is coming next.

QUESTION

Just what *is* going on? Draw some diagrams to show how the charge is being transferred. Why does the ball attract and then repel your finger?

You can also show charge transfer by using the little neon lamp attached to the plate. If you charge up the electrophorus and bring your finger up to the lead of the lamp, charge will flow to your finger. The lamp will light when this happens. (The lamp will be rather dim, so you may need to turn off the lights in order to verify what is going on.) When current flows in the lamp, it ionizes the neon gas, and makes it emit light.

Now here is the cool thing about the neon lamp:

when the lamp flashes, it flashes at only one electrode. This is the electrode that was the negative one—and so the electrode that electrons came from. So the bulb allows you to determine whether your electrophorus is charged up positively or negatively.

Charge up your electrophorus by directly transferring charge (the first technique you saw). How is it charged? Test with the neon lamp.

PREDICTION

Given what you have just observed, how should the electrophorus be charged when you charge it the second way—by induction? You will need to give some thought as to just how the charging takes place.

Make a prediction, and then test. Do you find what you expected?

And, Finally, the Answer to the Tape Question...

...is it in fact charged up positive or negative when you pull it off the roll?

QUESTION

How could you use your electrophorus to make this determination? Design a technique that will allow you to do this. Note: there are potential difficulties here. For example: you do not want to see if the tape is attracted to your electrophorus for your determination. This is because charges can move on the electrophorus, and so the results can vary. You can make it attract or repel, no matter how the device is charged. So you will need to test another way.

Summing Up

Ben Franklin, like his comrade Thomas Jefferson, was a very versatile man, making significant contributions in many areas. I have always felt a great affection for him as a historical figure, partially because he argued in favor of the wild turkey as our national symbol instead of the eagle, that he called a "bird of bad moral character." He was right about the eagle; I have seen eagles steal fish from smaller birds, and they often get their food this way. The turkey, I suppose, fit in much more with Franklin's slow-and-steady approach to progress.

Franklin's experiments in electrostatics were very much a series of such small steps. It was not that lightning struck; it was that he carefully built up a series of demonstrations that allowed him to determine quite a bit about how charges behave. In instruction, we follow a similar tack: the point of lab experiments in Physics is to give you a series of experiences that allow you to develop an understanding of the discipline. Each piece is important, which is why we stress the lab as we do. I am sure Benjamin Franklin would agree.

"Human felicity is produced not so much by great pieces of good fortune that seldom happen, as by little advantages that occur every day."

- Benjamin Franklin, *Autobiography*

Go in peace.

Coulomb's Law

Forces Between Charges

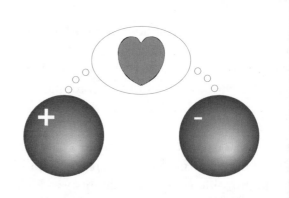

Opening Remarks

"What is the force holding together globular clusters? Love."

- Phil Battle, a student from my teaching days at Kenyon College.

People overemphasize the importance of gravity. Oh, it does hold us on the earth, and it does make the earth go around the sun, but as forces go it is a pretty wimpy one. When the different forces get together for a picnic at the beach, gravity is the 98 pound weakling that gets sand kicked in its face.

Consider this: if two grains of sand from this beach were held one meter apart, what would be the force of gravity between them? It would be far too small to be measurable. On the other hand, if the two grains of sand were stripped of their electrons and so were positively charged, they would repel each other with a force of about 3,000 million tons. This strength makes the electromagnetic force very easy to measure in the lab. By adding just a few spare electrons to objects, we can produce easily measurable forces between them.

Another difference between gravity and electromagnetic forces is that gravity is always attractive, whereas electromagnetic forces can be attractive or repulsive. This is what led Phil to make the conclusion noted above: all objects attract all other objects; why? Why do all the stars in a globular cluster attract all the other stars? Love, of course. How does this attractive force vary with distance?

If, as is often claimed, absence makes the heart grow fonder, the force should increase with increasing distance.

Alas, this is *not* the case for gravity or for electromagnetic forces: they both decrease with distance. The two grains of sand noted above, if put two meters apart, would repel each other with a force of only 750 million tons. Something you will explore in this lab is the manner in which the force between two charged objects varies as a function of distance. Ultimately, we will make a model - a formula - which describes this variation.

Theory

Coulomb's Law

Consider two point charges, charge q_1 and q_2, separated by a distance r along a line connecting their centers. Experimental observations show that the force between the two charges is directed along a line between the two charges and has the magnitude:

$$F = \frac{k|q_1||q_2|}{r^2}$$

where k is a constant. This relationship is known as Coulomb's Law. In this lab we will verify the form of Coulomb's law directly: we will show that the force between two charged objects is in fact proportional to the inverse of the square of the distance between them, i.e. the force varies as $1/r^2$.

16

Figure 1: Students who prefer to become more directly involved in the experiment will be provided with the necessary hardware.

There are excellent reasons to expect this to hold to a good accuracy; the electromagnetic force is transmitted by photons (light), and you know or will find out that the intensity of light drops off with the square of the distance. So, the $1/r^2$ variation is a purely geometrical effect; if the force was *not* proportional to $1/r^2$, this would tell us something very surprising. Very careful tests of the value of this exponent have been made. The most accurate means involve indirect measurements, related to Gauss' Law, which you will see later in the course. By such means it has been shown that the exponent in the Coulomb's Law expression must in fact equal -2 to an accuracy of one part in 10^{-16}! Your accuracy in this lab will most likely be somewhat less.

Practical Matters - The Spheres

The apparatus that you will use in this experiment appears as in Figure 2. Note that the objects to be charged are spheres; Coulomb's Law as stated only holds for point charges. As it turns out, using spheres is necessary, and does not affect the results of the experiment. The spheres are charged up to a given voltage that is limited by the high voltage power supplies that we have. As you will find out

later, a conducting sphere has a certain capacitance; if the sphere is charged to a voltage V, it will hold a charge Q as given in the following equation:

$$Q = CV$$

where C is the capacitance. The charge that is held is proportional to C, the capacitance. Capacitance is the capacity to store charge, and it is no surprise that a larger sphere can hold more charge than a smaller sphere: the charges can be farther away from each other on the surface of a larger sphere. The Coulomb's Law apparatus can measure only a limited amount of force; in order to get a measurable force, we need to charge up objects that can hold a reasonable amount of charge. So spheres that are small enough to look like point charges (i.e. with their radius very small compared to the distance between them) just won't work; their capacitance would be too small, and so would be the charge that they could hold at the voltage that we can charge them to. But it turns out that the size of the sphere has very little effect on the measurement. The charge will be spread out evenly over the surface of the sphere; as was the case for gravitation, the force from such a spherical shell will look like the force from a point at the center of the sphere. (This is actually a result of the form

17

of Coulomb's law, which is what we are testing, so this is perhaps a bit circular.) So we can treat the sphere as a point charge - and Coulomb's Law will apply as written, as long as we take the distance between the spheres to be the distance between their centers. The approximation only holds if the two spheres actually have uniformly distributed charges on their surfaces. In fact, if the spheres are close together, the charges on one will distort the distribution of charges on the other. So you will need to be aware that at short distances you might see some anomalous effect.

Practical Matters - The Torsion Balance

Look at the depiction of the apparatus in Figure 2 again. The repulsive force between the two spheres will rotate the hanging sphere to the left. The sphere will be brought back to its original position by rotating the top of the wire by an angle θ, as measured on the dial. It turns out that the force on the sphere will be proportional to this angle:

$$F = -c\theta$$

(Compare this to the $F = -kx$ spring force you have seen previously.) You could measure a value for c, but we will be content to realize that the force is proportional to the angle.

Experiments and Calculations

Necessary Equipment

Each group will need:

> Coulomb's Law apparatus
> Grounding wire and plug
> Kilovolt power supply and charging probe
> Macintosh computer

The basic piece of apparatus is the torsion balance and moveable sphere assembly detailed in Figure 2. Cautions to note: the wire is thin and quite fragile; take care with it. Do not touch the supports that hold the spheres, as this may contaminate them and cause charge leakage. Do not touch the spheres themselves. Basically, just keep your hands to yourself.

The power supply that you will be using to charge up the spheres will be set at a voltage of around 5000 V; a shock from this power supply would hurt, though it would not cause any damage as internal circuitry (in the power supply - not in you) limits the current. When you use the supply, always use it with the charging probe. The probe contains a very large resistance in the tip; this will eliminate the possibility of your getting any shock. Don't touch the tip anyway; doing so will charge you up, and will distort the results of the experiment.

Qualitative Investigations

Set up the equipment as described above. Notice that the power supply that you are using does not have an internal ground: in order to establish a voltage, one end must be grounded. As is shown in Figure 3, the probe can be maintained at either a positive or negative voltage. You must connect one terminal to ground, using the plug provided. If you ground the negative terminal, the positive terminal will be at a positive voltage. If you ground the positive terminal, the negative terminal will be at a negative voltage. If you ground the center terminal, the positive terminal will be at a positive voltage, and the negative terminal will be at a negative voltage. Voltages are always referred to this ground.

Given that you can produce either positive or negative voltages, you can charge the spheres up both positive, both negative, or one positive and the other negative. You can also charge one but not the other. If you are unsure as to how to make connections to do this, please ask your instructor for details.

QUESTION

By charging up the two spheres, show that the basic rules you have learned for the sense of the force apply: opposites attract, and like charges repel. How many cases do you have to try for a complete treatment of this problem?

Next, charge up the mounted sphere, but not the sphere that is free to swing; ground this sphere to

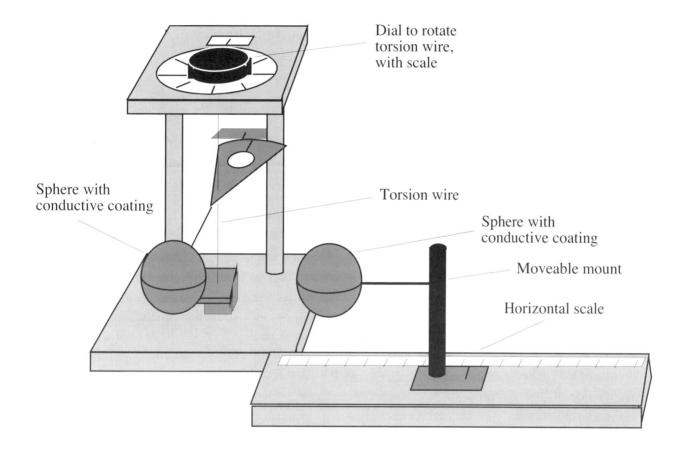

Dial to rotate
torsion wire,
with scale

Sphere with
conductive coating

Torsion wire

Sphere with
conductive coating

Moveable mount

Horizontal scale

Figure 2: A diagram of the equipment for the experiment. The wire is quite fragile; take care with it.
Natural Sciences students may note with pride that this equipment was purchased with Tech Fee money.
You may feel free to extract a levy from Engineering students using the equipment.

19

remove any charge. Move the mounted sphere close enough to the swinging sphere so that if there is any force it can be observed. Now watch what happens. The spheres should attract each other and touch. What happens after they touch?

PUZZLE

Explain what you just saw. Why do the two spheres initially attract each other? What happens after they touch?

PUZZLE

Given what you have just determined about the physics of the above situation attempt the following: charge up one sphere, and ground the other. It is possible to use the charged sphere and the grounding wire (which can take charges away) to charge up the uncharged sphere. Think about how you might do this, and give it a try.

PUZZLE

When you rub your feet on the carpet, you get charged up. Do you get charged up positively or negatively? Can you use your apparatus to determine the sign of the charge? Does everyone charge up the same way, or does it depend on your shoes? (Note: if the charge on you or on the ball is very much greater than the charge on the other, the stronger charge might just overwhelm the weaker charge, causing an attraction no matter what the signs of charge!)

Force vs. Distance

In order to make quantitative investigations, there are some initial adjustments that must be made to the equipment:

• Discharge the spheres with the ground wire (connected to the third pin of the electrical plug) that is provided. You should ground yourself regularly too.

• Slide the movable sphere as far back as it will go. Adjust the dial on the top of the torsion balance to read zero; rotate the clamp at the bottom of the torsion wire so that at this setting the sphere assembly is centered. (There is a mark on the assembly and a matching one on a clamp behind it that should line up.)

• Keeping the sphere assembly centered, slide the movable sphere up until the two spheres touch. The distance should be 3.8 cm; adjust the support if necessary. This is the diameter of one sphere; now the scale will give the distance between the two centers.

Now you are ready to take data. Set the distance between the two spheres to 15 cm. Place the probe in the high voltage output of the supply (red plug), set the voltage to its maximum value, turn on the supply, and charge up both spheres. You will have to leave the tip of the probe in contact with each of the spheres for a few seconds to insure that a good charge transfer takes place; turn off the supply when you are done. (This keeps the extraneous charge down.) After the spheres are charged, you should find that they repel each other. Adjust the torsion balance until the sphere assembly on the torsion wire is centered again; read off the angle from the dial. Record the angle and the distance between the spheres.

This is the basic procedure that you will use for other distances: set the distance, charge up the spheres, center the balance, and record the angle and distance. Make measurements like this for decreasing distances until you have at least 10 points covering a range down to 6 cm or so. As you take your measurements, observe the following precautions for best results:

• Ground yourself regularly to minimize the charge that you accumulate which will affect the experiment.

• When making adjustments, stay as far as possible from the apparatus, and keep your apparatus well away from the equipment of other groups.

• Hold the probe only at the back, as noted.

The forces that you are measuring are small, and electrostatic forces from other objects can ad-

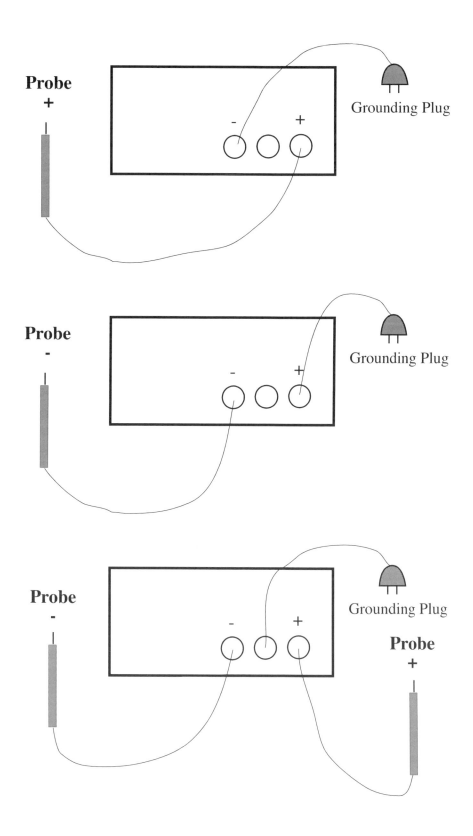

Figure 3: By adjusting which terminal is grounded, it is possible to get a positive or negative voltage on the probe. If the center terminal is zeroed, the probe can be made positive or negative. In this case, though, the voltage is across only half the supply, and so the voltage will be 1/2 of the dial reading.

versely affect the results. You should also keep the window closed so that air currents do not cause problems.

Once you have enough data, plot your results in the spreadsheet provided:

- Enter data for d (distance) and θ (proportional to force).

- Observe graph.

Next, make a model: what power of distance provides the best fit to the data? Is this what you expect from Coulomb's Law? This is the meat of this part of the lab: to show that the force falls off as the inverse square of the distance. There might be some surprises, though.... Some things to consider:

- Look at the graph for evidence of random and systematic error. Do you see any systematic errors at large or small distances? (There are good reasons to expect some deviations at small distances; can you give a reason?) Is the random error larger at one end or the other?

- Note the slope and the intercept, and discuss what, if any, physical meaning these quantities have. What additional pieces of information could you use?

Force as a Function of Charge

The charge should scale with the voltage, as noted in the theory section. The force between the equally charged spheres should vary as q^2, also as noted.

PUZZLE

How could you test this? Devise a plan to test whether the force varies as q^2 by making measurements at one distance and varying the voltage. If you have time, take several data points, define a new file in the graphing program, and graph your results. If you are short of time, take two data points and make a comparison with the expected behavior. Do the results appear as you expect? Think of any possible problems:

is all the expected charge transferred, etc, and discuss your results.

Summary

In this experiment you have become acquainted with the second of the fundamental forces of nature, after gravity. You can do a similar experiment for gravity, using a *very* sensitive torsion balance. The experiment is made difficult by the fact that gravity is the vastly weaker sibling of the electromagnetic force, which can tend to mask things.

Gravity makes things fall. The electromagnetic force also gives us electricity, chemistry, and light. Even the way the English language treats the two forces makes it seem better: "The atmosphere in the room was electric," vs. "The meeting was one of great gravity." But, gravity can curve space - and it is gravity that will determine the fate of the universe. So, if the Big Bang goes to the Big Crunch, gravity will have the last laugh.

Go in peace.

 *Experiments to Try at Home*

Pushing Water Around

As you discovered in the lab, charged objects can attract uncharged
objects. This is especially true if the uncharged objects are very
polarizable—that is, they develop a large polarization in the presence of
an electric field.

Water is quite polarizable, and so it can easily be attracted by charged
objects. Try this: run a comb through your hair briskly several times to
charge it up. Now hold the comb near a very thin stream of water from a
tap. You should be able to easily detect the force on the stream. What
happens to the stream when the comb is moved closer?

This might also be fun (but harder) to try with other liquids. Let me know
if you find anything surprising.

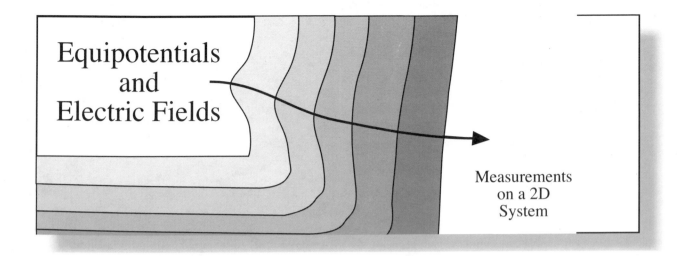

Equipotentials
and
Electric Fields

Measurements
on a 2D
System

Opening Remarks

Since this lab has a lot to do with Gauss' Law, perhaps we should open with a quotation from the man himself:

"It may be true that people who are *merely* mathematicians have certain specific shortcomings; however, that is not the fault of mathematics, but is true of every exclusive occupation."

- Carl Friedrich Gauss

Gauss was, after all, a mathematician, but we should not hold this against him. After all, his mathematics have proven to be quite useful for physics, so we can count him as a valuable ally. And at least he wasn't a chemist.

The intent of this lab is to help you visualize the electric field around different charged objects. In this lab, though, we will not measure electric fields; instead, we will make the easier measurement of potentials—which can be done with a voltmeter. With the voltmeter, you will find sets of points at which the potential is equal. These points will form so-called equipotentials - lines along which the potential is constant. Finally, these measurements will form the basis for deducing the electric field lines.

This is sort of an indirect measurement; we are getting at the field lines, which we are really interested in, through a measurement of equipotentials. The meter doesn't measure the field, but the measure-

ments you make with it will allow you to deduce the field.

Necessary Theory

Equipotentials: the gravitational analogy

In this lab, you will be plotting lines of constant electrical potential. It is worthwhile bringing up an analogy that you may have seen before: topo maps! Topo maps have lines of constant gravitational potential (that is, equal height) drawn on them. Here's an example: the first diagram in Figure 2 is a set of topographical lines depicting a mountain. Topographical lines on a map are lines of constant elevation. As gravitational potential energy is given by:

$$PE = mgh$$

these lines of constant height are thus lines of constant gravitational potential. It may be useful to think of this gravitational analogy when you are doing this lab.

We can also make a gravitational analogy with the electric field. Consider the gravitational force on a unit mass on Mount Renal. The downhill force is greatest where the contour lines are closest together, and the direction of the force is perpendicular to the contours. This analogy holds with the electrical case also.

Since water flows downhill, a lake on a map is an

24

Figure 1: Alone at work on a slow Friday afternoon, Chester has a revelation.

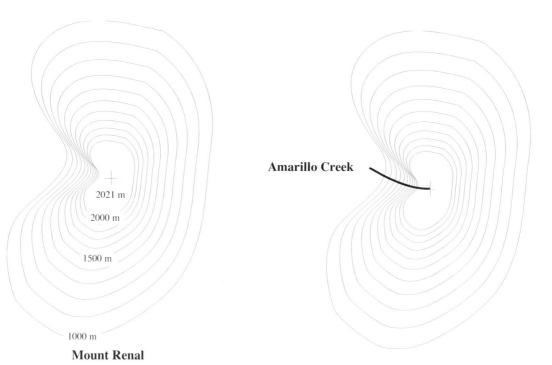

2021 m

2000 m

1500 m

1000 m

Mount Renal

Amarillo Creek

Figure 2: The first diagram shows the contour lines of Mount Renal, the amazing kidney shaped mountain in the Organ Mountains of New Mexico. Each contour line represents a line of constant height, and thus constant gravitational potential energy: thus, these are equipotential lines. Hikers will know that if you walk along one of these lines, you are not going up or down: you are at a constant elevation. Now consider walking uphill; the direction of the force is clearly perpendicular to the contour lines. To walk uphill as directly as possible, you turn to be perpendicular to the contours. Hikers will also know that the steepest climb will be where the contour lines are the closest together. The lines of force are thus perpendicular to the contours, and they are stronger where the contours are closer together.

When water flows downhill, it tends to flow in the direction of the net force, i.e. perpendicular to the contours. It will also flow most rapidly where the contours are closest together, where the force is the greatest. It is thus no surprise to find Amarillo Creek flowing along the path shown.

equipotential surface. And, since trains can't go up steep grades, train tracks often follow equipotential lines on maps. Actually, when I bicycled cross-country with some friends after college, we found this useful; we found that by following a set of tracks we could keep at a pretty constant potential. This was important, as we were out of shape after four years of doing physics to the exclusion of almost everything else.

Drawing Field Lines: a Quick Recap

In this lab you will use the equipment to draw equipotential lines for different physical systems. To your diagram of equipotentials, you will add field lines. Recall the basic rules for this:

- Field lines can only begin and end on charges (and conductors).
- Field lines are perpendicular to equipotentials.
- Conductors are equipotentials; thus, field lines are perpendicular to conductors.

If you follow these rules, you will find that the field lines are closest together where the equipotentials are. Thus, given the above discussion, we can say:

- The field strength is greatest where the field lines are closest together.

As you are drawing field lines, keep these rules in mind, and try to consider the physical meaning behind them.

Gauss' Law

A possible set of field lines is shown in Figure 3. A circle is overlaid. This is the 2D version of a closed surface; thus, the flux must be zero, as the circle encloses no charges. What does this mean in terms of the field lines? Is this condition satisfied? You will have a chance to consider such issues in the lab.

Experiments and Calculations

Equipment Needed

There will be eight sets of the following equipment placed around the lab:

> Overbeck field mapping apparatus
> Multimeter (use as voltmeter)
> Power supply
> Connecting cables

The heart of the field apparatus is a graphite-coated plate. Onto the surface of the graphite an electrode configuration is painted with conducting paint. The electrode configurations available are sketched later, with some hints and tips as to what to look for in each case.

This plate is screwed to a plastic base; screws connect the electrodes in the plate to connectors on the base. A power supply is connected to these electrodes, setting them to different potentials. This sets up an electric field in the plate, for which equipotentials can be measured and plotted. The region in between the electrodes on the graphite sheet is weakly conducting, allowing a measurement of the potential at each point. You will make measurements of the potentials at different points by using a voltmeter, as shown in Figure 4. Figure 5 shows a side view of the probe that is actually used to make contact with the plate. To measure a set of points with the same potential, you will move the probe to find points for which the meter reads the same.

In practice, the plate is clamped to the bottom of the base, and a piece of paper put on the top. The probe is on a holder that touches the top and the bottom. A hole in the top of the holder that is directly above the probe tip allows you to make a mark on the paper when the voltmeter reads a certain value. In this way you can plot out the equipotentials directly on a piece of paper.

There are some precautions to note here. The voltmeter should give a voltage reading everywhere. If it reads zero, you should look for a loose connection. And the potential jumps around quite a bit even for a small distance change. You will find

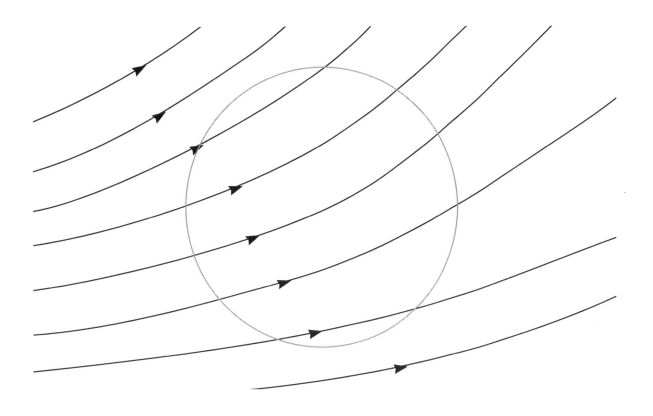

Figure 3: A set of field lines is illustrated. A circle, a 2D closed surface, is overlaid. Consider how many lines go into the circle, and how many exit. What does this imply about the flux?

in practice that you will need to reduce the sensitivity of the voltmeter in order to be able to make measurements. You can do this in two ways:

- Reduce the voltage of the power supply. If the full swing is smaller, so will be the small variations.

- Put the voltmeter on the 200 V scale, instead of the 20 V scale. This means that you will lose a decimal place. Instead of reading, say, 2.51 V, you will read 02.5 V. This will make the readings more stable.

I hope you can make some sense of this from this description and the accompanying diagrams. If not, it will all become clear when you come to lab and get to see the stuff. (Really!)

Procedure for one plate

There will be eight bases around the room with four different types of electrode arrangements, two of each. Choose one to start with, and proceed as follows:

1) Depress the base gently so that the rubber hemispheres on the four corners come up slightly. Place a piece of paper on the base and slide the edges under the hemispheres; release pressure on the base so that the paper is held in place.

2) Lift the base to see what electrode arrangement you have. There will be a template on the table that duplicates this. Place it gently over the metal pegs on the base. Use it to trace out the electrode configuration that you have on your paper.

3) You are now ready to begin measuring equipotentials. The plate, probe, galvanometer and power supply should be connected as shown in Figure 4. Place the probe over the plate as shown in Figure 5. Be gentle! You should adjust the pressure of the probe on the plate by adjusting the thumb screw on the top arm of the probe. There should be enough tension that the probe on the bottom surface makes reliable contact, but not so much that the thumb screw that touches the top surface drags the paper around.

4) The probe is connected to a voltmeter, which tells you the potential at the point that the probe touches. Pick a good spot on the plate to start making an equipotential line, and note the potential here. Now mark with a pen through the hole in the top of the probe the position of the probe. Next, move the probe until you find a nearby point that has the same potential. Do this for several points; you need enough points to be able to draw an equipotential line. Be sure that you use enough points that you can adequately tell how to draw the line!

5) Pick another spot on the plate to start, and record another equipotential line. Repeat this procedure until you have traced out several sets of points. You may want to use different color pens or some notation to keep track of which points go with which equipotential. Think about what lines you want to draw. You should take at least six sets of points, and probably more. Don't take all of your measurements on one side; spread them out a bit. But you might want to have more data in areas where things are more interesting. Keep tracing sets of points until you have enough to give you a very good picture of what the equipotentials look like.

6) Remove the paper and disconnect the power supply. Connect the points of each equipotential by a smooth curve.

7) Now deduce the field lines for the case you are considering. Recall the rules noted above for deducing field lines from equipotentials.

Observations

Once you have made a nice diagram, make some observations and conclusions. There are tips for each of the systems given below.

28

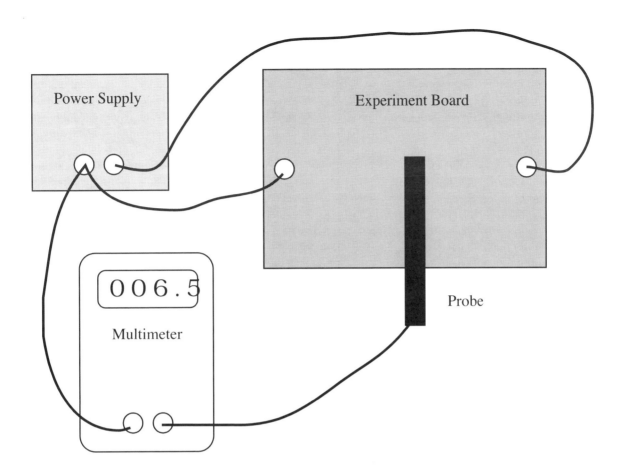

Figure 4: The power supply is connected across the experiment board. This means that the voltage on the plate on the bottom of the board will vary from 0 V to the voltage that the power supply is set to. You will measure the voltage at individual points by using the probe connected to the multimeter.

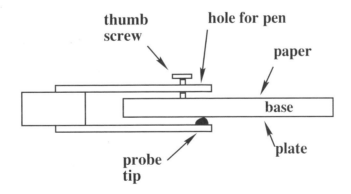

Figure 5: The probe is meant to gently contact the plate that you will make measurements on. You can adjust the thumb screw to get enough pressure to hold the probe in place, but be gentle! Too much pressure will damage the equipment.

The following plate has two small spherical charges:

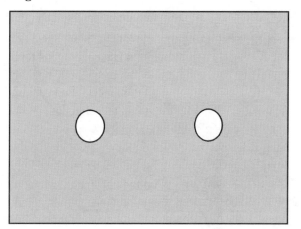

You should have a pretty good idea of the field lines for this case.

PUZZLE

Where is the field strongest? Where is it weakest? How can you use Gauss' Law to show that the two conductors are equally charged?

This plate represents a parallel plate capacitor:

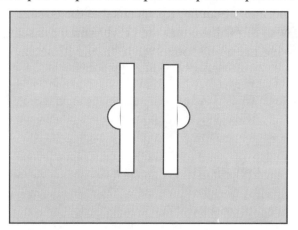

Again, the field lines should be familiar.

PUZZLE

Where is the field strongest? Where is it weakest? If a circle is drawn around both plates, what should be the flux?

This plate represents two charged conductors with a region of conductor (light gray) and a region of insulator (dark gray):

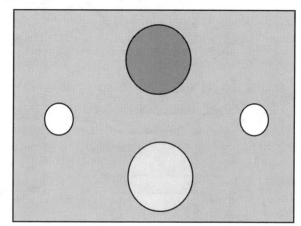

PUZZLE

How will the conductor and insulator affect the field lines? How can you tell which is the conductor and which is the insulator? If you draw a circle around the conductor, what should be the flux? Can you draw a circle that includes only part of the circle that has a nonzero flux?

This plate is a 2D analog of a Faraday Ice Pail.

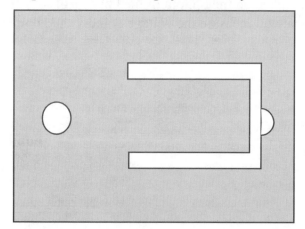

PUZZLE

Recall that the field inside a conducting shell is zero. Since the right conductor is 3/4 of a closed shell, the field will be shielded from the region inside it. What does this imply for the equipotentials and the field lines? Where is the field strongest? Where is it weakest? Where does the charge collect on the ice pail surface?

Futher Investigations

We have another set of electrode arrangements for which measurements are made in a very different manner. These arrangements, and some details about them, may well make it into your lab.

Electric Fields Lab

Electrode Arrangement: Shielding

General Procedures

1) Set power supply to 12.0 V.

2) Attach power supply to the two plates, with the red lead to the top plate and the black lead to the bottom plate. The rectangular box should not be connected.

3) Attach the black lead of the meter to the black lead of the power supply (this is the ground lead.)

4) Use the red probe of meter to measure potentials. Set the meter to "200 V" scale, so that there is only one digit after the decimal point. Press the probe gently but firmly to the paper to measure potentials.

5) Use the paper grid to note the positions of equipotentials. Sketch the equipotentials and use these to determine field lines.

Specific Procedures, Predictions, and Questions for This Case

1) Do a quick sketch of the situation on the graph paper provided.

2) Do a quick sketch of equipotentials at 2.0, 4.0, and 6.0 V. The situation is symmetric; estimate what the equipotentials at 8.0 and 10.0 V will look like.

3) Do a quick sketch of the field lines. They aren't straight; do they bend toward or away from the conducting box in the center of the electrodes?

4) Now think about why the field lines bend as they do. Sketch where charges will be on the conducting box. Note that the net charge on the box will be zero, but there will be positive and negative charges collected at different points. Do the field lines begin and end on charges as they should?

5) Measure the potential at several points inside the conducting box. Do you see any variation? Explain. What is the field inside the box? How do you know this?

6) Suppose you were in an airplane (which has an aluminum skin) and the plane wass hit by lightning. Would you have anything to worry about?

Electric Fields Lab

Electrode Arrangement: Parallel Plates

General Procedures

1) Set power supply to 12.0 V.

2) Attach power supply to the two plates, with the red lead to the top (or right) plate and the black lead to the bottom (or left) plate.

3) Attach the black lead of the meter to the black lead of the power supply (this is the ground lead.)

4) Use the red probe of meter to measure potentials. Set the meter to "200 V" scale, so that there is only one digit after the decimal point. Press the probe gently but firmly to the paper to measure potentials.

5) Use the paper grid to note the positions of equipotentials. Sketch the equipotentials and use these to determine field lines.

Specific Procedures, Predictions, and Questions for This Case

1) Do a quick sketch of the situation on the graph paper provided.

2) Do a quick sketch of equipotentials at 2.0, 4.0, 6.0, 8.0 and 10.0 V. What are the equipotentials at 0.0 V and 12.0 V? Note them.

3) Do a quick sketch of the field lines. Are they shaped more or less as you expect?

4) Double the voltage to 24.0 V. How does this affect the equipotentials? Use your probe to quickly determine where the 2.0, 4.0 and 6.0 V equipotentials are. (Just do one point - don't draw the whole lines.) What has happened to the spacing between the equipotentials? What does this tell you about the electric field between the two plates?

5) Use your probe to look at the regions above and below the two plates. Is there much variation in potential? What does this tell you about the field in these two regions?

Electric Fields Lab

Electrode Arrangement: Dipole

General Procedures

1) Set power supply to 12.0 V.

2) Attach power supply to the two plates, with the red lead to the top (or right) plate and the black lead to the bottom (or left) plate.

3) Attach the black lead of the meter to the black lead of the power supply (this is the ground lead.)

4) Use the red probe of meter to measure potentials. Set the meter to "200 V" scale, so that there is only one digit after the decimal point. Press the probe gently but firmly to the paper to measure potentials.

5) Use the paper grid to note the positions of equipotentials. Sketch the equipotentials and use these to determine field lines.

Specific Procedures, Predictions, and Questions for This Case

1) Do a quick sketch of the situation on the graph paper provided.

2) Do a quick sketch of equipotentials at 2.0, 4.0, 6.0, 8.0 and 10.0 V. The situation is symmetric; estimate what the equipotentials at 8.0 and 10.0 V will this might allow you to save some effort!

3) Do a quick sketch of the field lines. Do they appear as you expect?

4) Suppose we were to identify one of the electrodes as having a "+" charge and one as having a "-" charge. Which one would be which?

5) Where is the electric field strongest in this case? Where is it weakest? Explain how you know this.

Electric Fields Lab

Electrode Arrangement: Dipole with Conductor

General Procedures

1) Set power supply to 12.0 V.

2) Attach power supply to the two plates, with the red lead to the right electrode (the circular one) and the black lead to the left electrode (the circular one). The rectangle is a region of conductor that will not be connected to the power supply - but will affect equipotentials and fields.

3) Attach the black lead of the meter to the black lead of the power supply (this is the ground lead.)

4) Use the red probe of meter to measure potentials. Set the meter to "200 V" scale, so that there is only one digit after the decimal point. Press the probe gently but firmly to the paper to measure potentials.

5) Use the paper grid to note the positions of equipotentials. Sketch the equipotentials and use these to determine field lines.

Specific Procedures, Predictions, and Questions for This Case

1) Do a quick sketch of the situation on the graph paper provided.

2) Do a quick sketch of equipotentials at 2.0, 4.0, 6.0, 8.0 and 10.0 V.

3) What is the potential at the conducting electrode at the bottom? Does this vary from point to point? Measure and see. Why should you expect this? In fact, it should be an equipotential - you can use this to help sketch field lines.

4) Do a quick sketch of the field lines. You know what the field of the dipole should look like; how does the presence of the conducting electrode at the bottom change things? How do the field lines behave in the vicinity of the conducting electrode? What does this tell you about the charges on the electrode? Where are they? What is the net charge on the electrode?

Electric Fields Lab

Electrode Arrangement: Field Near Point

General Procedures

1) Set power supply to 12.0 V.

2) Attach power supply to the two plates, with the red lead to the top (or right) plate and the black lead to the bottom (or left) plate.

3) Attach the black lead of the meter to the black lead of the power supply (this is the ground lead.)

4) Use the red probe of meter to measure potentials. Set the meter to "200 V" scale, so that there is only one digit after the decimal point. Press the probe gently but firmly to the paper to measure potentials.

5) Use the paper grid to note the positions of equipotentials. Sketch the equipotentials and use these to determine field lines.

Specific Procedures, Predictions, and Questions for This Case

1) Do a quick sketch of the situation on the graph paper provided.

2) Do a quick sketch of equipotentials at 2.0, 4.0, 6.0, 8.0 and 10.0 V. Note: the situation is symmetric right to left. You should only have to sketch half of each equipotential. Where are the equipotential lines most closely spaced? What does this tell you about the electric field? Where is it strongest?

3) Do a quick sketch of the field lines. Where are the field lines closest together? What does this tell you about the strength of the field? Where is it strongest?

3) Estimate - using numbers - the size of the field right near the point. How does this compare to the field away from the point? (Hint: the electric field is in units of V/m. How does this allow you to determine the field value?)

4) If a spark were to jump from the top plate to the bottom plate, where would it be most likely to jump? Explain.

Electric Fields Lab

Electrode Arrangement: What it Looks Like

General Procedures

1) Set power supply to 12.0 V.

2) Attach power supply to the two plates, with the red lead to the top plate and the black lead to the bottom plate.

3) Attach the black lead of the meter to the black lead of the power supply (this is the ground lead.)

4) Use the red probe of meter to measure potentials. Set the meter to "200 V" scale, so that there is only one digit after the decimal point. Press the probe gently but firmly to the paper to measure potentials.

5) Use the paper grid to note the positions of equipotentials. Sketch the equipotentials and use these to determine field lines.

Specific Procedures, Predictions, and Questions for This Case

1) Do a quick sketch of the situation on the graph paper provided.

2) Do a quick sketch of equipotentials at 2.0, 4.0, 6.0, 8.0 and 10.0 V. Where are the equipotential lines most closely spaced? What does this tell you about the electric field? Where is it strongest?

3) Do a quick sketch of the field lines. Where are the field lines closest together? What does this tell you about the strength of the field? Where is it strongest?

4) Estimate the value of the electric field at the top of the person's head and at the top of the tree. (Hint: the electric field has units of V/m. Think about how you could use this to estimate the field.)

5) If lightning went from the top plate to the bottom plate, where would it be most likely to strike?

Electric Fields Lab

Electrode Arrangement: Coaxial Conductors

General Procedures

1) Set power supply to 12.0 V.

2) Attach power supply to the two plates, with the red lead to the top inner electrode and the black lead to the outer electrode.

3) Attach the black lead of the meter to the black lead of the power supply (this is the ground lead.)

4) Use the red probe of meter to measure potentials. Set the meter to "200 V" scale, so that there is only one digit after the decimal point. Press the probe gently but firmly to the paper to measure potentials.

5) Use the paper grid to note the positions of equipotentials. Sketch the equipotentials and use these to determine field lines.

Specific Procedures, Predictions, and Questions for This Case

1) Do a quick sketch of the situation on the graph paper provided.

2) Do a quick sketch of equipotentials at 2.0, 4.0, and 6.0, 8.0 and 10.0 V. What is the general shape of the equipotentials? (Note: if you think about symmetry, you can save yourself a lot of work here!) Does the spacing of the equipotentials vary? What does this tell you about the field strength?

3) Do a quick sketch of the field lines. What is their general shape? What about the spacing of the field lines? Where are they closest together? Farthest apart? Where is the field strongest? Weakest?

4) What is the potential inside the inner conductor? What is the field inside?

5) What is the potential outside the outer conductor? Does it vary? We said that the field should be zero inside a conducting shell - but this was only for external charges and fields. If there are charges inside the shell, there can be a field inside the shell. Can this field get outside?

Electric Fields Lab

Electrode Arrangement: Faraday Ice Pail

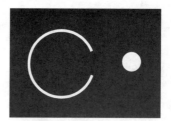

General Procedures

1) Set power supply to 12.0 V.

2) Attach power supply to the two plates, with the red lead to the right plate and the black lead to the left plate.

3) Attach the black lead of the meter to the black lead of the power supply (this is the ground lead.)

4) Use the red probe of meter to measure potentials. Set the meter to "200 V" scale, so that there is only one digit after the decimal point. Press the probe gently but firmly to the paper to measure potentials.

5) Use the paper grid to note the positions of equipotentials. Sketch the equipotentials and use these to determine field lines.

Specific Procedures, Predictions, and Questions for This Case

1) Do a quick sketch of the situation on the graph paper provided.

2) Do a quick sketch of equipotentials at 2.0, 4.0, and 6.0, 8.0 and 10.0 V. (Note: there is some symmetry here that can save you some work.) This might not be enough to allow you to sketch the field lines; sketch one or two more equipotentials if necessary.

3) Do a quick sketch of the field lines. Where is the field strongest? Weakest? Inside the partial circle, is the field weak or strong? Why? (We said that a conducting shell could provide shielding against external fields. In this case, we have almost a whole shell, which provides some shielding.)

4) The field lines begin and end on charges. This tells you something about the charges on the partial circle electrode. Where are the charges? Explain why this is so.

5) Is the field larger near the opening in the partial circle electrode, or well inside? How could you tell?

Summing Up

In this lab you use an apparatus to measure the equipotentials resulting from different configurations of electrodes. From these equipotentials you deduce the field lines for the different cases, and make comments and conclusions based on your observations. Gauss' Law figures prominently; you should have some chances to see that it works as described for the situations you are working with. The point of the experiment is to help you visualize some of the concepts that you will be working with in class.

The model that you are working with is a 2D model: you are working with a conductive sheet. By using a tank of salt water you could do the same thing in three dimensions; if you feel the desire to fill up your bathtub and try it out, we would be pleased to lend you a voltmeter and any other necessary equipment.

Oh, yes: since I started with a quote that is not particularly kind toward mathematicians, I will end with one that is not so kind to other people.

"Those who cannot cope with mathematics are not fully human. At best they are tolerable subhumans who have been taught to bathe and not make messes in the house."

- Robert Heinlein

Go in peace.

Field, Potential and Gauss' Law

Firming up Some of the Basic Concepts

Opening Remarks

"When *I* use a word," Humpty Dumpty said, in rather a scornful tone, "it means just what I choose it to mean - neither more nor less."

- Lewis Carroll, *Alice's Adventures in Wonderland*

Some of the basic concepts in electricity and magnetism are rather abstract; no one has ever seen an electric field, nor a voltage. (You can feel a current, though - if you are in doubt of this, stop in my office and we will do a little demonstration.) And the words that we use for them - such as "potential" - are words that get used for other things too. But we mean something very specific when we use these words. It is the point of this lab to help you get a better feeling for what we mean physically by the terms field, potential, and potential difference.

This lab will be done using a computer simulation. Even though this seems artificial, it really is not. It is a real experiment - you can set up any situation that you want, and it will evolve according to the laws of physics.

Necessary Theory

The necessary theory for this section is the basics of fields and potentials - which will be covered nicely in your textbook and in class.

Experiments and Observations

Necessary Equipment

This experiment is done entirely on the computer:

Mac computer running EM Field program

The following exercises will run a bit differently than the standard labs that you have done. They are more a sort of "guided inquiry" in which you will be asked to do certain things and then comment on what you observe.

Field: What is the Meaning?

We are going to start out easy with this one.

• Start the "EM Field" program, and choose "2D Charged Rods (with Gauss' Law)" from the "Sources" menu.

• Select a single charge of +5, and place it in the center of your working area. You will use this simple situation as the basis for all of the upcoming exercises.

Of course, in my day, we had to walk to school. No bus for us! And it was five miles if it was a foot. And it was uphill. Both ways, going to school and coming home. In the snow, too.

Figure 1: No matter what grandpa says, this sort of scenario is ruled out by the way potential energy works. If you start and end at the same point, you have done no net work. This path independence is also true for electrostatic potential.

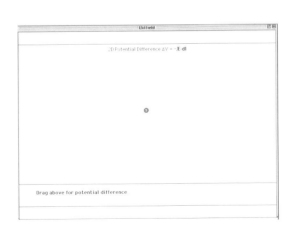

• Now, choose "Field Vectors" from the "Field and Potential" menu.

• Click in the window to place field vectors all around. Each of them will show the direction and magnitude of the electric field at one point.

QUESTION

What is the meaning of the electric field at some point? How would you measure it in practice?

Keep the setup just as you have it; you will use it in the next section.

Potential Difference

Field is the force per unit charge. Force times distance, as you learned last semester, is work. So, when you take a positive charge and move it in the opposite direction of the electric field, you need to apply a force - and so you are going to do some work.

This means that you will be raising the potential

energy of the charge. But rather than speak in terms of potential energy, we speak in terms of *potential*: the potential energy per unit charge.

For starters, though, we will talk about potential *difference*: the difference in potential between one point and another point.

• Choose "Potential Difference" from the "Field and Potential" menu.

• Click on one point, and drag the mouse to another point. As you drag, the program will graphically represent the line integral of the electric field. This is the potential difference - related to the work done moving in the field.

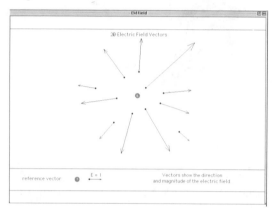

• Now, pick two points in the window to measure the potential difference in between. If you move parallel to the field, you get large differences in potential as you go; if you move perpendicular to the field, you get smaller differences in potential as you go. Trace the mouse across two completely different paths between the two points you have chosen, in one case trying to move parallel to the field as much as possible, and, in the other, trying to move perpendicular to the field as much as possible.

QUESTION

What do you notice about the potential difference along the two different paths?

QUESTION

Can you explain why they should be related in this way? Be as complete as you can.

Since the potential difference is only a function of

the end points of the path, not the shape of the path, it is possible to define a potential at any point as the difference from a particular point. This is the crux of the next section of the lab.

Potential

It is possible to define a potential at any point as the potential difference between the point and some fixed reference point. You could choose any point as the reference; in principle, you could measure all potentials from that purple spot on the inside of your fridge where you left that burrito over Christmas break last year, where the fungus left that interesting stain. But it is nice to choose a point with some more physical meaning.

• Choose "Potential" from the "Field and Potential" menu.

• Move the mouse around, and see what the potential is at different points. Where is the reference point? The potential should be zero here. Can you deduce where it is? (Hint: you can't get to it on the screen.) Think back to what you know about gravitational potential; does this help?

QUESTION

So, where is potential measured from? Why is this reasonable in terms of what you know about electric fields?

Gauss' Law

Gauss' Law is a rule about the flux of electric field through a surface: it is related to the amount of charge inside the surface.

This program is done in 2D, not 3D, so you will draw a line instead of a surface, but the idea is the same: the flux through the path you draw is related to the charge inside.

QUESTION

Restate Gauss' Law for a 2D situation.

• Choose "Flux and Gauss' Law" from the "Field and Potential" menu.

• Draw a closed path that does not include the charge. As you draw, the flux will be calculated and shown graphically. How can you see that sometimes the flux is positive and sometimes it is negative? What is the net flux? How is this related to the charge contained in the closed path?

• Draw other closed paths that include or do not include the charge. If things get too messy, choose "Clean up Screen" from the "Display" menu.

• Now, choose "Clean up Screen" from the "Display" menu to get a fresh start. Draw two Gaussian paths, one that includes the single charge and one that does not. Now add a charge to the system, using the "Add More Charges" option from the "Sources" menu. How does the flux change for the two paths you have drawn?

• Move the new charge around; try putting it in one of the paths. How does this change the flux in each case? Does it do what you expect?

Grand Final: the Challenge Game

OK, now that you know a bit more about fields and potentials, it is time for a challenge. Choose the "Challenge Game" option from the "Options" menu.

QUESTION

What would Coulomb's Law be for this 2D situation? In 3D, the field varies as one over the square of the distance. How about in 2D? Why? You will need to know this in order to determine magnitudes!

• Choose the "1 Charged Rod" option, and follow the rules for the game. In principle, you should be able to determine the location and the sign of the charge with just two measurements. Can you do it?

• Now try the "2 Charged Rod" option.

• If you are up for a real challenge, try the n charged rods case - you don't know how many there are, so this one takes a bit of work!

Summing Up

This lab is a bit different than the standard ones that you do. It doesn't involve any meters or real measurements. On the other hand, it uses a simulation package that lets you experiment, and it is very powerful in helping you understand and visualize the meanings of the different quantities under discussion - which is the point of the lab, really.

Go in peace.

Parallel Plate Capacitor

Getting a Charge out of Things

Opening Remarks

"With these Experiments, how many pretty systems do we build."

- Benjamin Franklin, discussing his investigations into electricity

For many years, electricity was used more or less as a parlor trick. Static charges could be produced by various means that could charge things up, make sparks fly, make objects attract and repel each other, and so on. But it was not possible to get enough charge to do anything all that useful. Eventually the battery was developed. This could produce continuous current, albeit at low voltages. This development began to make the use of electricity practical for doing useful work.

For storing electrical energy, before the battery came the Leyden jar: a thin-walled glass vessel, with metal foil on the inside and the outside. It was basically a capacitor: two conducting sheets separated by an insulating layer. Static charge could be repeatedly placed on the inner conductor; the device had the ability to collect and accumulate a good deal of charge. As a matter of fact, it could shock the pants off people when discharged. The capacitor was thus really the first electrical device, and it was instrumental in showing that electricity could be used for more than amazing your friends at parties.

The interesting thing about the Leyden jar was the thinner the glass, the more charge was held.

By using a thin jar and a source of high voltage, it was possible to get enough energy stored to be lethal. Capacitors can store a lot of energy for a long time; this is why there are warnings on the cases of television sets and other such appliances that go like: "WARNING; DANGEROUS VOLTAGES INSIDE." What they mean is, "There are capacitors in here that get charged up to very high voltages, and since you don't know a capacitor from a bar of soap, if you open the case you will most likely touch it and shock your pants off." These are big capacitors, and can store lots of energy. Some older appliances with really huge capacitors would actually run for a while after being unplugged as their capacitors ran down.

In this lab, we will not be playing with any capacitors like this. We will use a relatively modest air-spaced parallel plate capacitor. The nice thing about the capacitor we will use is that you can accurately vary the distance between the plates; you will thus be able to verify that the capacitance is larger for a smaller separation. Not only that, you will be able to make a model for the variation and test it out.

The voltages to be used are not high enough to shock your pants off, but they can give you a good jolt that is an experience that is worth not having. So enjoy, but be careful.

Figure 1: Though Faraday Associates spent millions of dollars developing and marketing the perpendicular plate capacitor, they never achieved the success they hoped to. (Thanks to Roger Tinkoff.)

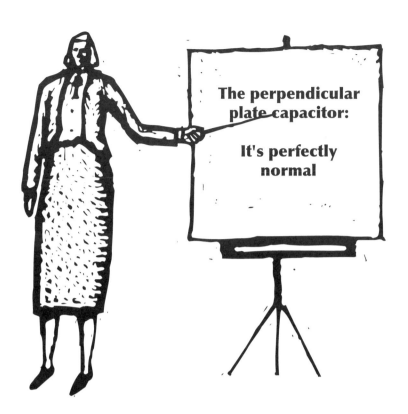

Figure 2: The basic setup of the experiment. Two parallel plates are connected up to a high voltage power supply set to a voltage V. Current will flow; the plates will thus charge up to equal and opposite charges +Q and -Q. The charge that accumulates is proportional to the capacitance: Q = CV. What could be simpler?

High voltage supply set at voltage V

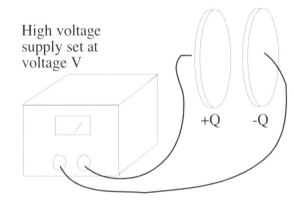

+Q   -Q

Necessary Theory

Suppose we have a high voltage power supply that puts out a voltage V. We connect its leads to two separated, insulated conductors, as in Figure 2. A current will flow for a short time, until a voltage develops between the plates that opposes the voltage of the power supply. A charge Q will flow; the two conductors will charge up to equal and opposite charges +Q and -Q.

This set of conductors forms a capacitor. A capacitor stores charge at a voltage. If the conductors are removed from the power supply, they will stay charged up; the voltage between them remains the same. The voltage and the charge are proportional to each other: if you double the voltage, you double the charge that is stored. The amount of charge that is stored is proportional to a constant associated with the plates called the capacitance, C:

$$Q = CV$$

C has the units of farads, after Michael Faraday. In terms of other units,

$$1 \text{ farad} = 1 \text{ coulomb/volt}$$

thus a 1 F capacitor charged up to 1 V would hold

a charge of 1 C. 1 C is a lot of charge; you will get a chance to use a 1 F capacitor this semester, and you will find that it holds an impressive amount of energy.

It is worthwhile noting that any two conductors separated by a space or an insulator make a capacitor. For instance, the wires that are attached to the capacitance meters that you will use have a certain intrinsic capacitance that must be corrected for.

The capacitance of the parallel plate capacitor will be measured two ways: first, by making a direct measurement of the charge stored at some voltage and using the basic defining relationship of capacitance, and second, by taking the easy way out and using a capacitance meter.

The capacitance of a parallel plate capacitor will be quite small for reasonable plate sizes and separations. For the capacitor you will use in lab, with plates of radius 10 cm, setting the plates to a separation of 1 cm gives a capacitance of about 28 picofarads - i.e. 28×10^{-12} farads. Thus, even at a voltage of 1000 V the capacitor will only hold a charge of 28 nanocoulombs - a small charge indeed. In order to get a charge large enough to measure accurately we will have to use a large voltage.

The basic setup that you will employ for the first part of the experiment appears as in Figure 3. The high voltage supply is set to a voltage of around 5000 volts. The three position switch in the center controls what the capacitor is connected to. If it is to the left, the capacitor is connected across the power supply. If it is in the center, the capacitor is not connected to anything. If it is to the right, the capacitor is connected across the coulomb meter. A measurement will proceed as follows:

i) Switch is set to left; capacitor charges up.

ii) Switch is quickly flipped to the right and then back to the center.

During step i), the capacitor will charge up to the voltage of the power supply. This voltage can be read off the meter or dial of the supply and will be kept fixed during the course of the experiment.

During step ii), the capacitor is briefly connected across the coulomb meter. When the coulomb meter is connected to the capacitor, the charge from the capacitor flows to the meter and its value is displayed. Note that the measurement operation discharges the capacitor. The value of the transferred charge is displayed, in units of nanocoulombs.

In the lab, the first measurement that you will want to make is to verify that the basic formula defining the capacitance has some rhyme and reason. As

$$Q = CV$$

doubling the voltage should double the charge stored; C is a constant. You should do a quick test to see that this is in fact true.

Once you have verified this, you can use this expression to calculate the capacitance from the charge acquired at a given voltage:

$$C = Q/V$$

The capacitance can also be measured directly with the meter. You can measure the capacitance as a function of distance, and graph it. The goal is to make a model for the variation of capacitance with distance, and to test it.

Lastly, you can verify the effect of a dielectric on capacitance. Suppose you take two plates that are charged to a given charge. If a dielectric is inserted between the plates, the field between the plates will be reduced. This means that the voltage between the plates will be reduced. From the above formulas, you can see that this means that the capacitance is increased. Commercial capacitors almost always have an insulating dielectric between the plates. There are two benefits: one, the capacitance is increased, and two, they are easier to make, for obvious reasons.

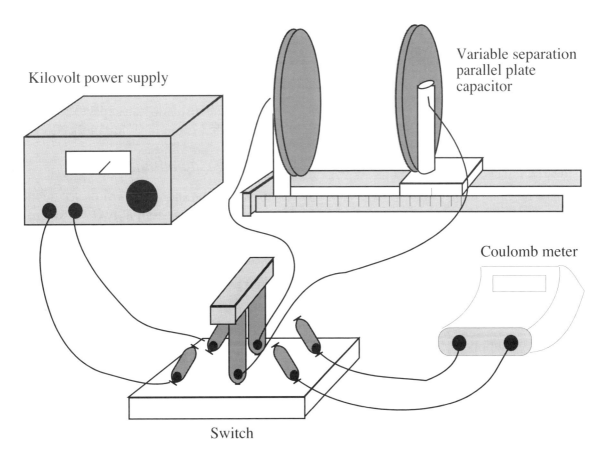

Kilovolt power supply

Variable separation parallel plate capacitor

Coulomb meter

Switch

Figure 3: This is a sketch of the basic apparatus that will be used in the experiment. The capacitor is connected to the center terminals of the switch. If the switch is thrown to the left, the capacitor is connected to the high voltage supply, and charges up. If the switch is thrown to the right, the capacitor is connected to the Coulomb meter; it is discharged to the meter, and the charged is measured. In order to measure the charge accurately, the switch must be thrown quickly. And in order to not get a shock, you must avoid touching the metal parts of the switch - use caution!

Experiments and Calculations

Equipment Needed

The set of apparatus for this experiment:

> High voltage power supply
> Variable separation parallel plate
>   capacitor
> Coulomb meter
> Switch and connecting wires
> Capacitance meter
> Aluminum plates with leads
> Grounding wire with plug
> Plastic plate (dielectric)

There are some precautions to be observed while using this equipment. The high voltage supply is current-limited, so it is not able to kill you or even injure you, but, as noted, a jolt from it is not pleasant. Don't touch the "hot" parts of the switch, the contacts, or the capacitor when it is charged up. If you are worried about the capacitor holding a charge, turn off the power supply and touch it with the grounding wire; this will eliminate any residual charge.

The coulomb meter is a very sensitive instrument; to measure 10^{-9} C of charge on a microfarad capacitor means measuring voltages on the order of millivolts. Clearly, the coulomb meter will not be pleased if it suddenly finds itself connected across the full 5000 V of the power supply. As a matter of fact, it will then be in a state that is technically referred to as "fried" or "wasted." This is obviously to be avoided. If you do not alter the arrangement of the equipment there is no way to connect the coulomb meter in this way, so don't change the connections.

Getting Started

Set the capacitor at a separation of a cm or so. Make sure the cables are connected as shown in Figure 3, then proceed as follows:

i) There is a red button on the meter that resets it to zero; press this button to reset. The meter reads out in nanocoulombs (10^{-9} coulombs); there is no way to adjust the scale. It may well start charging up or down once you have reset it; if so, reset it again just before you make your measurement.

ii) Set the power supply to 5000 V. (Use less if arcing or discharging occurs.) Charge the capacitor and measure the charge acquired as noted above:

- Set switch to left.
- Flip switch quickly to right, then back to center.

Leave the capacitor connected to the coulomb meter for several tenths of a second; this is long enough to transfer the charge, but not long enough to pick up too many stray charges. If you leave the meter connected, these stray charges will accumulate and distort the measurement.

Try this measurement a few times, shorting out the coulomb meter each time. It will not zero itself for a new reading; it will just keep acquiring additional charge. Are the measurements reproducible? Work out a technique for doing the measurement that gives the same results reliably.

Capacitance Formula

The basic equation describing capacitance:

$$Q = CV$$

implies that the charge stored on the capacitor is proportional to the voltage to which it was charged. This is easy to test with the setup that you have; please do so.

PUZZLE

Think about how to do this. The graphing program can be used to make a graph of Q vs. V; what result do you expect? If you get a line, what is the meaning of the slope?

Computing Capacitance

For a plate separation of 1 cm or so, deduce the capacitance of the system in two ways:

i) Charge up the system to a known voltage. Discharge to the coulombmeter and measure Q. From this data you can deduce C.

ii) After making sure the capacitor is discharged (use the grounding wire), measure the size of the plates, and compute the capacitance from the formula for the parallel plate capacitor.

PUZZLE

Do your results agree? You will probably find that they don't. Which one is higher? Why? Think about it, then go on to the next section.

Stray Capacitance

Recall that any two separated conductors make a capacitor. This means that the wires, the contacts on the switch, etc. will all have some capacitance. This will alter the readings that you get. You can demonstrate the existence of this stray capacitance and get some idea of its magnitude by measuring the capacitance of the system without the parallel plates. You can do this with the capacitance meter, or by using the coulombmeter and voltage supply as before. Make this measurement, and discuss your results.

Actually, the capacitance meter can be used to make a good demonstration of this stray capacitance. Try this:

- Zero the capacitance meter with the leads not connected to anything, and well separated.

- Now twist the leads (gently) around each other. What happens to the reading?

44

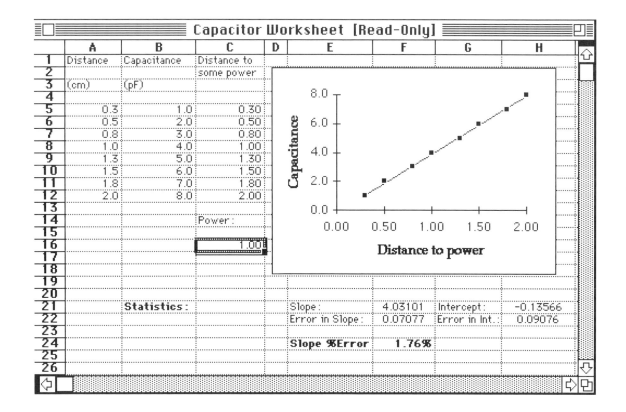

	A	B	C	D	E	F	G	H
1	Distance	Capacitance	Distance to					
2			some power					
3	(cm)	(pF)						
4								
5	0.3	1.0	0.30					
6	0.5	2.0	0.50					
7	0.8	3.0	0.80					
8	1.0	4.0	1.00					
9	1.3	5.0	1.30					
10	1.5	6.0	1.50					
11	1.8	7.0	1.80					
12	2.0	8.0	2.00					
13								
14			Power:					
15								
16			1.00					
17								
18								
19								
20								
21		Statistics:			Slope:	4.03101	Intercept:	-0.13566
22					Error in Slope:	0.07077	Error in Int.:	0.09076
23								
24					Slope %Error	1.76%		
25								
26								

Figure 4: You will enter data for distance and capacitance into a graphing program to determine a power law fit to the data. By looking for the best power law fit to the data, you can deduce the relationship between the capacitance and the distance.

Why?

This shows the importance of the stray capacitance. There is no need (and really no good way) to calculate the stray capacitance, but you can measure and correct for it.

Air-spaced Capacitor

Disconnect the high voltage source, the switch and the coulombmeter from your capacitor, and measure its capacitance directly with the capacitance meter. Make measurements of the capacitance as a function of the separation between the plates. Be sure to take the stray capacitance into account! (You could, for example, zero out this component on the meter.) Next, analyze your data:

• Enter the data into the computer, and note the graph produced.

• Manipulate the data so that a straight-line graph is obtained. You will determine what power of the distance the capacitance is proportional to.

Then, you can make connections with the physics:

• What is the meaning of the slope of your line? Given the measurement of the size of your plates that you have made, this should enable you to give a measured value for a fundamental physical constant. Does the value you obtain agree with the accepted value?

• What is the meaning of the intercept of your line, if it is nonzero?

Turning Dialectic into Dielectric (Thanks to Priscilla Laws for this Title)

This section is one to be done if there is time, or it may be used in place of an earlier section. It duplicates a lot of the material of the earlier sections, but with much simpler (read: cheaper) materials. It makes for a more intuitive and interesting experiment.

Of course, it is possible to make a capacitor out of

much more prosaic materials. Take the following materials:

- Textbook
- Two sheets of aluminum
- Ruler
- Capacitance meter

and see if you can devise tests to illustrate the following:

- The variation of capacitance with distance between plates
- The variation of capacitance with area of plates.

Along the way, you can determine the dielectric constant of the paper used in the textbook you use for the experiment.

A reminder: in everything that follows, make sure that you consider the intrinsic capacitance of the meter and the wires! You can zero the meter, or you can subtract it off, but ignore it at your peril.

Use the aluminum to make two plates of a capacitor. You can sandwich them in the pages of your book to make a capacitor. The paper makes a very nice insulator, and, as a very nice side benefit, you can very accurately measure the separation of the plates.

PUZZLE

You only have a ruler to make distance measurements. How can you use this device to make an accurate measurement of the thickness of a sheet of paper in your book? If you are careful, you can easily measure the thickness to an accuracy of 1% or so—plenty accurate for this experiment.

Something to consider: the smaller the plate separation, the larger the capacitance—and, therefore, the more accurate the measurement.

Make a series of measurements of capacitance vs. distance. Do the measurements show the predicted relationship for capacitance with distance? That is to say, does the capacitance decrease inversely with distance?

QUESTION

How could you show this with a graph? What do you plot to test if this relationship is valid?

Once you have made distance measurements, pick a good thickness and vary the area of the plates to test the variation of capacitance with plate area. You can do this by adjusting how much of the plate lies between the pages.

QUESTION

At some point, the plate area will be so small that the formula that you have been given for capacitance will no longer apply. When does this happen?

Again, give some thought as to how to show—graphically or otherwise—whether the linear relationship between capacitance and plate area is followed.

Finally, for one good measurement of distance, area, and capacitance, compute the dielectric constant for the paper in your book. How does this compare to the dielectric constant of air? Water? You might also try different kinds of paper; is coated paper different from uncoated (like the lab manual)?

This exercise is left purposely quite open: there is a lot that you can do with it! The point is to allow you to be creative and to do some interesting physics with some very simple tools. And, to be honest, to use the phrase that titles this section, whose cleverness I appreciate. I am always a sucker for wordplay.

Summing Up

"Thunder is good, thunder is impressive; but it is lightning that gets the job done."

- Mark Twain

This lab was an introduction to the physics of the capacitor. A capacitor, as a device, is usually meant to be a discrete electrical component with a well-defined value for C, its capacitance. But, as we have seen, any two separated conductors can act as a capacitor. Examples:

• The earth and clouds (and, if enough charge builds up, lightning will result);

• Your car (on insulating rubber tires) and the ground. You build up a fair amount of charge by friction in some cases.

• Two wires in a circuit.

Capacitance. You just can't get away from it.

Go in peace.

"Dear Professor Hartwig," Elizabeth wrote, "since seeing your remarkable demonstration of the power of the Leyden jar, I can think of nothing else. I hope that someday all people may perform experiments on capacitance in our institutions of higher learning. This would truly be a great thing for our country."

Current and Voltage

Generators, motors, bulbs, buzzers and stuff

Opening Remarks

"Electricity: Where Does it Go After it Leaves the Toaster?"

- Title of article in *The Journal of Irreproducible Results*

The two primary electrical quantities, voltage and current, and the relationship between them, are often the source of a large amount of confusion. Members of the general public tend to think of "electricity" as a sort of a fluid that gets pumped from the electric company into their home. The quantity of this fluid is variously measured in volts, amps, or watts, much like volume can be measured in liters, gallons, or cubic meters. "115 volts of electricity comes into your house"; this is the sort of statement most people will accept as making some good sense.

There are two basic models for what happens to the electricity once it comes into your house. Many people believe that things work like in Figure 2: the electricity is used up in the toaster. It comes in, but doesn't come back out, so there is only a need for one wire.

A more sophisticated view is that we have a circuit in which electricity comes in, goes through the toaster, then goes back out. Then, the electricity is returned to the power company to be "recharged." The article referred to above (which, as the journal title might lead you to believe, is intended to be humorous) states that the power company just sends out the same electricity over and over again, and never generates any new electricity. "In fact," the authors state, "the last time any electricity was generated in the United States was 1937."

Well, we sophisticates with some physics education know that things are a bit more complicated than this. What do you mean by electricity? As noted, we have two basic electrical quantities:

- current / flow of charge

- voltage / potential; causes charge to move

In this lab, you will use a device that gives immediate feedback to you as to the voltage and the current in a circuit. You will explore parallel circuits, series circuits, and circuit elements such as capacitors, motors, generators and light bulbs. The goal is for you to develop some *qualitative* understanding of the complex interrelationships of voltage and current, and some sense of the related concept of resistance. So, someday, when a child, nephew, niece, or grandchild asks the question:

"Where does the electricity go after it leaves the toaster?"

you will be in a position to answer. And remember—you heard it here first.

48

Figure 1: In this early print, Volta (from whom we get the term volt) is showing the operation of his pile (now called a Voltaic pile) to colleagues. This was the first demonstration of sustained current flow; it was produced by electrochemical rather than static means. The pile was the forerunner of the battery. I taught in a British system school at one point; when we discussed the history of this particular device, students got quite a charge out of it. The reason is that in British English the term "pile" is their term for

Figure 2: The basic naive models of electrical conduction have electricity coming in through a single wire to the toaster, where it is used up, as below. As we know, there are in fact two wires, and a circuit is made. This is the basis of a more advanced naive model: that the electricity goes through the toaster and back to the power plant where it is "recharged." But we must use some care in stating what happens. What are you really purchasing from the electric company? Electrons? Give this some thought.

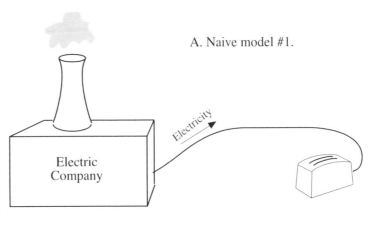

A. Naive model #1.

Electric Company

Electricity

Necessary Theory

The Genecon

The basic device for today's lab is the Genecon. This is a hand-cranked DC generator that looks like a ray gun out of a bad science fiction movie (such as Leonard Nimoy's film debut, "Zombies from the Stratosphere.") The generator has a handle on one end, and two wires that come out of the other. The key properties of the Genecon are:

- The voltage that is put out by the Genecon is roughly proportional to the speed that you turn the crank. If you need a higher voltage, just crank faster.

- The current that is put out by the Gene-

con is roughly proportional to the force necessary to turn the crank. The harder you find yourself having to push, the more current is coming out.

By cranking the Genecon at a constant speed, you can produce a constant voltage. And, by noting the force necessary to turn the crank, you can deduce the size of the current flowing in the circuit.

Circuits

In the lab you will explore a number of different circuits. In each case, you will be asked to make a prediction as to what will happen: how hard will it be to turn the crank, how bright will the bulb light, etc. Try to use the basic theory for this that you have seen in class; it will not be reviewed here.

Experiments

Necessary Equipment

Each group will be provided with the following set of equipment. The symbol for each piece of equipment that will be used in diagrams is also provided.

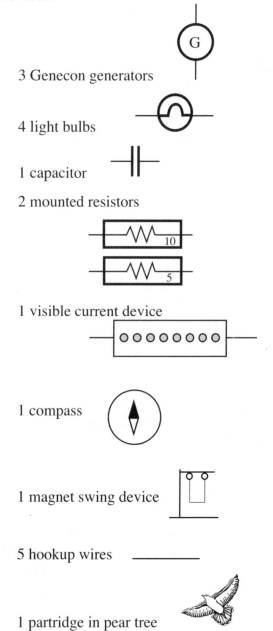

3 Genecon generators

4 light bulbs

1 capacitor

2 mounted resistors

1 visible current device

1 compass

1 magnet swing device

5 hookup wires

1 partridge in pear tree

All of the small pieces will be provided to you in a box; please see to it that no pieces go missing. Keep them in the box when not in use.

A description and discussion of each device follows.

 The Genecon is a hand-cranked generator that is quite robust, but is intended to be used in certain ways. Please be gentle with them: do not crank them too fast, do not crank them too hard, and generally treat them with respect.

Recall the important rules about the Genecon:

• Voltage is proportional to cranking speed
• Current is proportional to cranking force

One other key thing to note about the Genecon: as with all generators, if you pull a lot of current out of it, the output voltage drops. Keep this in mind; if you get a result that seems odd in some way, you might think if this output drop for the Genecon might be the culprit.

 The light bulbs are rated at a voltage so that they can be easily lighted, but this means that they can be easily burned out. If the bulb seems too bright, slow down! It probably is.

The capacitor is 1.0 F; something like this would have been unheard of twenty years ago. The capacitors can be damaged by too much voltage, which can come from a Genecon cranked too fast. As you use the capacitors, please try as much as possible to note the polarity. The positive terminal is the one that is not connected to the case. Current is intended to flow in to this terminal if possible.

 These symbols represent resistors mounted on little blocks of wood. You will have two of these: a small resistor (labelled "5" in the manual) whose actual value will be labeled on it, and a large resistor (labelled "10" in the manual) whose actual value will be labelled on it also.

As current flows through the resistors,, they will heat up; you can sense the temperature change with your finger. If you don't sense anything, try placing the resistor lightly against your forehead, which is much more sensitive.

The hookup wires have alligator clips on both ends (people in Africa call them "crocodile clips") and can be used to connect bulbs, capacitors, etc.

The visible current device is a device that works like a wire - but with a difference. A pattern of lights moves inside the device that shows you the direction of the current and the magnitude: a faster moving pattern means a greater current.

(This is, of course, how real currents work: there are only so many free charge carriers, so if there is to be more current, they will need to move faster!)

The Experiments: Procedures

In the experiments that follow, it is *crucial* that you use the following approach:

i) Read over what is being asked.

ii) With your lab group, predict what the outcome of the experiment will be.

iii) Test your prediction.

iv) Explain what you observe, and why or why not it does or does not agree.

The hypothesis step is particularly crucial. Be sure that you make a prediction before you make any measurements. Record these as you go along, together with the observed results and any explanation. This is to be done as a group with your lab partners.

The Experiments: Details

First Steps

Build the following circuit:

i.e., the Genecon not connected to anything. Crank the Genecon at about one turn per second. Note how much force you must use to do this.

Now, connect the two leads of the Genecon together. What do you observe? In the first case, you were applying a voltage, but since no current was flowing, no work was done. Once you connect the leads, current flows. Then, you are doing some work—which you can feel! The harder it is to turn the crank, the more current that is flowing. Keep this in mind.

Setting Standards

In order to have a standard setup to compare to, make the following circuit, which we will call the "standard circuit."

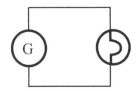

Establish a standard cranking speed that keeps the bulb lit, but not too brightly. One or two times per second seems to work well. Get a rhythm that you can reproduce; this will be your "standard cranking speed." When you use the same speed on future circuits, you can be sure that the voltage out is the same. Leave this circuit connected for now.

Series Circuit

With the remaining bulbs and Genecon, you will build the following series circuit:

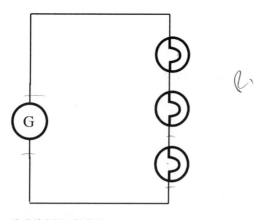

PREDICTION

Before you build the circuit and turn the crank, make the following predictions:

• When cranked at the standard cranking speed, will the bulbs be brighter, dimmer, or the same as the bulbs in the standard circuit?

• Will the crank be easier to turn, harder to turn, or require the same effort to turn as in the standard circuit?

Make some justification for your predictions.

Once you have made your predictions, test them. You still have the standard circuit set up, so you can test one circuit after the other.

Were your predictions correct? Make some comment. If you found something different than you expected, explain.

QUESTION

Is the current larger in the series circuit or in the standard circuit? (You should have already thought about this!) If you aren't sure, hook up the visible current device in each circuit, and see - in which circuit does the light pattern move fastest?

Parallel Circuit

Next, you will rearrange the bulbs in the above circuit to make a parallel circuit:

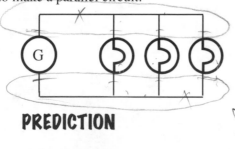

PREDICTION

Before you build the circuit and turn the crank, make the following predictions:

• When cranked at the standard cranking speed, will the bulbs be brighter, dimmer, or the same as the bulbs in the standard circuit? The series circuit?

• Will the crank be easier to turn, harder to turn, or require the same effort to turn as in the standard circuit? The series circuit?

Make some justification for your predictions.

Once you have made your predictions, test them. You still have the standard circuit set up, so you can test one circuit after the other.

Were your predictions correct? Make some comment. If you found something different than you expected, explain.

More Fun with Series and Parallel Circuits

PREDICTION

For the following circuit predict which bulb will be the brightest:

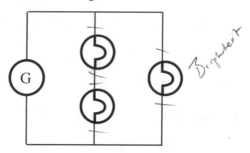

Build it and test. What did you find?

Now...

PREDICTION

...predict which bulb will be the brightest in this circuit:

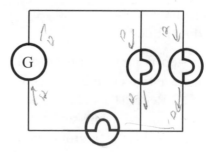

Build it and test. Again, what did you find?

Some Like It Hot

Now, take two Genecons and hook one to each of the mounted resistors you have been given. One will have a high resistance and one a low resistance.

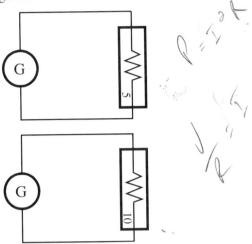

PREDICTION

Predict:

• For which circuit will it be harder to crank at the standard cranking speed?

• Which temperature strip will heat up faster at the standard cranking speed?

Test your predictions.

Yet More Fun with Series and Parallel Circuits

PREDICTION

If the two resistors are connected in series:

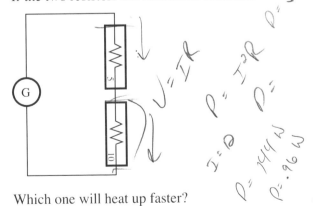

Which one will heat up faster?

Make a prediction and test. (Note: it may take a while to see the effect.)

How about if the two strips are connected in parallel:

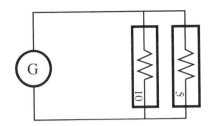

PREDICTION

Which one will heat up faster?

Make a prediction and test.

Where Has All the Energy Gone?

If you connect your two Genecons together...

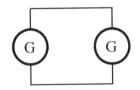

PREDICTION

...when you crank one, what will happen to the other? Predict and test.

Do the two turn at about the same speed? One of the Genecons is working as a generator, the other as a motor. As we will see later in the semester, the two devices are very closely related.

Now, if you put a resistor (light bulb) in the circuit...

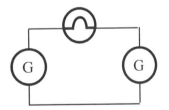

PREDICTION

...how will this change things? Will the second Genecon (the one that is working as a motor) go slower, faster, or the same as before? Make a prediction and test.

(Note: the cranking speed is crucial in this case.)

PUZZLE

Did the light bulb light in this case? Is this surprising? Now try this: hold the crank of the "freewheeling" Genecon, so that it does not move. Does the light bulb light now? What is going on? Explain. You may wish to use the visible current device to help you sort this one out. (Hint: the voltage across the Genecon depends on how fast the crank is going - whether you are turning the crank or whether it is being turned by an applied current)

Capacity of a Capacitor

When you connect your Genecon to the 1 F capacitor you have been given:

it is important to get the polarities correct: make sure that current flows into the positive terminal of the capacitor. (Your instructor will have details.)

PUZZLE

Build this circuit and turn the crank at the standard speed. What happens to the necessary force as time goes on? Explain. Now, let go of the crank. What happens? Explain what is going on, in terms of energy and in terms of current. What direction is current flowing in the circuit before and after you stop turning the crank? (Hint: you may want to use the visible current device in this circuit to help you sort things out. How does the current change, in magnitude and direction, as you crank up and then let go?)

The RC Circuit

Keep a Genecon hooked up to your capacitor:

Turn the crank for a while until the force needed to turn the crank goes way down; at this point, you will know that the capacitor is essentially fully charged. Now, quickly, disconnect the wires to the capacitor.

EXPERIMENT

Connect the charged capacitor to a light bulb, with nothing else in the circuit. Notice how the light bulb appears as time goes on; explain what is happening.

Draw a qualitative graph of the brightness of the light bulb (which is a measure of the current) as a function of time. How does the brightness fade - does it drop quickly to zero, or does it have a long tail, getting dimmer, dimmer, dimmer....? Think about it, and make a sketch. Remember the form of this graph; this is something that you will look at again later.

The key thing to note is this: when you connect the capacitor across the light bulb, the voltage on the capacitor causes a current to flow. Of course, this current discharges the capacitor. And as the capacitor discharges, its voltage becomes less. As the voltage becomes less, so does the current - so the capacitor discharges more slowly. It still discharges, but the rate of the discharge is less. And as it discharges more, the rate decreases more....

Remember this; you will see it again.

Putting it all Together

Next, put a light bulb in the circuit:

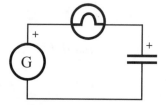

PREDICTION

Make the following predictions:

• As you crank, what will happen to the brightness of the bulb?

• When you let go of the crank, what will happen to the brightness of the bulb, right after you let go, and later on?

Test these predictions and explain what you see.

Connections with Magnetism

This material should properly go in a later part of the course, but we are here now, so what the heck.

Here's the thing: electricity is connected in a very fundamental, one might even say intimate, way with magnetism. The exact nature of this connection is something that you will spend some time exploring later in the semester. For now, just do the experiments, record what you see, and file away the information. When your instructor starts talking about magnetism in class, he or she will most likely start by talking about connections with electricity. You can nod your head and smile knowingly.

Currents and Compasses

Take a Genecon, and use a hookup wire to connect the two leads. Now take the wire and wrap it repeatedly around your compass, with the wire parallel to the needle, like so:

Hold the compass level, so that it can swivel. Normally, the compass lines up with the magnetic field of the earth. Now turn the crank on your Genecon. What happens now?

PUZZLE

Now, complete the following sentence:

"Currents produce _____ fields."

This is a rule that you will learn more about.

Magnets and Currents

Next, take your Genecon and connect it up to the so-called magnet swing device. The swing is a wire which is connected to two hooks; the wire is free to swing, while staying connected to the hooks.

Be sure that the wire is free to swing and is making good contact, and crank your Genecon. What happens? Now turn the crank the other way. What happens now? Turn the crank back and forth; if you are careful to match your cranking speed to the speed of the swing, you can get a good amplitude going!

PUZZLE

Now, complete the following sentence:

"Magnets make forces on _____ ."

This is another rule you will learn more about later. In the meantime, here's something to ponder: motors have magnets in them....

And, a Chance to Be Creative

If you have some time, you can try other combinations of the circuit elements that you have been given. Try to make circuits to do something. Make predictions as to what you think will happen, then see if this is what you observe. Feel free to borrow items from other benches - as long as they end up back where they came from!

If you have any concerns that what you are about to do will break something, ask for advice. And please do not get too excited when you are cranking the Genecons: they are not meant to hold up to rough treatment, and the current produced could well burn things out.

Be creative — and enjoy!

Summing Up

Most people truly do not know the answer to the question posed in the first sentence of this document. And I think that is why people are scared of electricity: people are often scared of that which they do not understand.

Even though we don't understand how our toasters work, let alone our computers, people are pretty happy to use these devices on a daily basis. And as technology has become more global, it is amazing how it has changed things. Right as I sat down to write this, I got an e-mail from a former student, a woman who is now in the Peace Corps in Namibia. It is truly a small world these days, and, if we are less scared of things that we better understand, we might hope that as we get to know each other better, we will live more peaceably.

Of course, the point my former student's e-mail was that she was being evacuated from her post, due to an insurgency. It is a small world these days, but perhaps not small enough. Technology will not do the job for us, though I do hope that it can make it easier.

"Peace is not made with friends. Peace is made with enemies."

- Yitzhak Rabin

Go in peace.

Resistors and Resistivity

Opening Remarks

"[A] physicist who professed such ideas was unworthy to teach science."

- German Minister of Education, reacting to Professor George Simon Ohm's discovery of the law which bears his name.

Of course, we have a somewhat different impression of Ohm's investigations. The concept of resistance is a central one in electrical work; though resistance may not always be a constant, the ratio:

$$R = V/I$$

may always be computed, and is a valuable measure.

In this lab we will look at how resistance varies as a function of geometrical shape, look at parallel and series combinations of resistors, and measure the changing resistance of a light bulb filament.

How much more fun could you have in two hours? (Don't answer that.)

Necessary Theory

Resistance and Resistivity

Ohm's Law tells us that for most material elements in a circuit, the voltage across the element is proportional to the current through it:

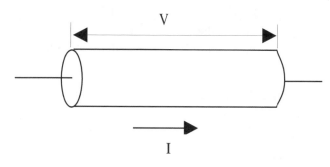

$$V = RI$$

The constant of proportionality is called the resistance. The resistance of a physical element depends on a physical property of the material, called the resistivity, and the geometric structure of the element. Suppose we have two identical cylinders, one made of copper and the other made of silicon. Silicon has a much higher resistivity, and so the silicon cylinder will have a much higher resistance. On the other hand, if we consider two cylinders made of silicon, one long and thin:

and one short and fat:

the long, thin cylinder will have the greater resistance. For cylindrical elements, and for others with a uniform cross section, the resistance varies as a function of the physical dimensions as follows:

Figure 1: There are many egregious science puns to be found in this vale of tears, but no area is as fertile for this as circuits. A few of the more dismaying examples are reproduced for your inspection at right. (I would welcome your submissions for future issues of the lab manual.) People seem to find puns on "ohm" particularly, shall we say, irresistible?

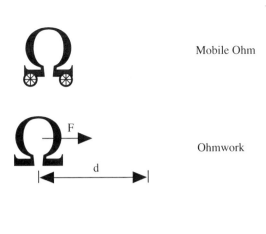

Mobile Ohm

Ohmwork

A pair of shorts

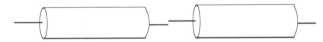

$$R = \frac{\rho L}{A}$$

ρ is the resistivity, L the length, and A the cross sectional area.

Parallel and Series Combinations of Resistors

We can use the above information to derive the rules for connecting resistors in series and in parallel. Suppose we have two resistors with the same cross section connected in series:

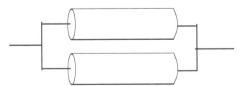

The resistance will be the resistance of the total length:

$$R = \frac{\rho}{A}\left(L_1 + L_2\right) = R_1 + R_2$$

This is just the formula for a series combination of resistors; we can take it as a general rule. If we consider two resistors of the same length connected in parallel:

The resistance of the whole is seen to be the resistance of the whole area:

$$R = \frac{\rho L}{\left(A_1 + A_2\right)}$$

$$\frac{1}{R} = \frac{A_1}{\rho L} + \frac{A_2}{\rho L} = \frac{1}{R_1} + \frac{1}{R_2}$$

And, we end up with the formula for the parallel combination of resistors, which we can take as a general rule.

This is a different manner of deriving these formulas than you will see in most texts; there is, as usual, more than one path to the truth.

In this lab, you will use your knowledge of parallel and series combinations of resistors to deduce the contents of a box.

What is the Resistance of a Lamp?

Ordinary carbon-film resistors are designed to keep a constant resistance under normal operating conditions, which will include a variety of different voltages and currents. You can see this by considering the first graph in Figure 2. A plot of I vs. V is a nice, straight line: resistance is a constant.

For light bulbs, this is not true. The problem is the temperature: a light bulb filament will heat up when current passes through it; as a matter of fact, this is what it is designed to do. The filament is in an evacuated bulb, so the filament's temperature changes quite a bit as the current does; it can only lose heat by radiation, which is quite inefficient.

For a 12 V bulb, varying the voltage from 0 to 12 V may cause a change in temperature of the filament by as much as a factor of 10, from about 300 K to about 3000 K. For the metal filaments in most lamps, the resistance is proportional to the temperature; thus, the resistance will also vary by a large amount.

The varying resistance of a lamp filament may be seen in the second graph in Figure 2; a graph of current vs. voltage is not a straight line. The resistance increases as the voltage does.

There are two logical investigations one could make concerning the resistance of the lamp:

i) Make a model for how the resistance varies as a function of voltage

ii) Given that the resistance of the lamp filament varies proportionately to the temperature, make measurements at small and large voltages to deduce the temperature of the lamp filament under normal operating conditions.

Time permitting, you can try both of these in the lab.

Experiments and Calculations

Necessary Equipment

Each group will be provided with the following equipment:

> 0 - 15 V variable power supply
> 2 hand-held DVM's (digital voltmeter)
> Unknown resistor box
> Lump of Play-Doh and working tray
> Metal plates for attaching to Play-Doh
> Ruler
> Wire brush to clean plates
> Lamp on component board
> Connecting cables

The DVM is a device that you will use regularly this semester. If you are uncertain as to its operation, ask your TA for details. A DVM can measure voltage, current or resistance, with some caveats:

• If a DVM is set to act as an ammeter, its resistance is very low. It *must* be placed in series with a larger resistance; if it is placed in parallel with a voltage source, a large current will flow though it. This will distort the measurement, and may well damage the DVM (or at least blow a fuse).

• If a DVM is set to measure voltage, it must be placed in parallel with the component across which it is to measure the voltage. If it is placed in series, the large resistance will keep any current from flowing, which will give bizarre results for the circuit.

Generally, when measuring the resistance of a device in a circuit, you should connect the power supply, resistor, and meters as follows:

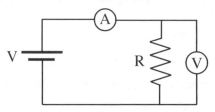

Note the above cautions, and you will not have any trouble. If you are in doubt, before turning on your power supply, turn the voltage all the way down. Once the supply is on, gradually raise it, and watch to see that everything is in order.

As the DVM's can measure resistance directly (by applying a known voltage, and measuring the current), it is possible to measure the resistance in a circuit, as above, or to make a direct measurement just using the resistance mode of the meter. You will do both of these in the lab. One caution: don't use the resistance mode unless the device you are measuring is completely disconnected from the circuit. Other sources, meters and devices in the circuits could screw things up.

Another thing: though we like to encourage creativity and individual expression, we will request that you not use the Play-Doh for anything other than the experiment at hand. Don't build little sculptures; this dries the Play-Doh out. When you are not doing experiments on it, keep it in the can.

58

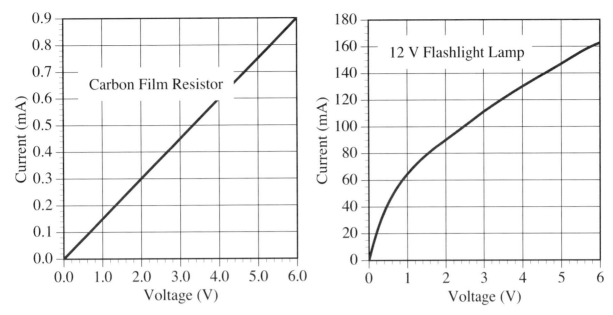

Figure 2: Graphs of I vs. V for a carbon-film resistor (left) and a flashlight bulb (right). For the resistor, the graph is a straight line: the resistance is constant over the range of voltages in the graph. For the bulb, the graph is not a straight line: the resistance varies over the range of voltages tested. The resistance is defined by the ratio V/I; can you see that this increases as the voltage does?

Resistance and Resistivity

In this section of the lab, you will pass a current through a chunk of Play-Doh. By measuring this current and the voltage across the Play-Doh, you will be able to deduce the resistance of the piece of Play-Doh you have set out. This resistance will vary as a function of the color of the Play-Doh (can you see why?); it will also vary as a function of the geometry of the particular piece you are using. For instance, a long, thin cylinder will have a greater resistance than a short, fat one.

There are some practical difficulties in making these measurements. In order to eliminate the effect of the changing conditions at the electrodes (which otherwise would create a big problem), you will have to make what is known as a "four point" measurement. You will need to make Play-Doh electrodes to connect up the Play-Doh, and measure voltage and current as outlined in Figure 3. There will be a great change in the resistance at the place where the metal leads touch the Play-Doh. This will affect the current. And, since you are measuring the voltage across just the piece of interest, it will change too. The ratio of the two should stay constant, though; this is the reason for doing this four point technique.

After you have set up your Play-Doh electrodes, take the remaining Play-Doh that you have been given and roll it out into a cylinder. (You will be given a tray to do this in; please be careful not to get the Play-Doh all over everything. Feel free to leave to wash you hands at any time.) Make rough measurements of the diameter and the length. Pass a small current through your sample. Place the probes along the cylinder; you can measure the voltage between any two points. What is the voltage end-to-end? What is the current? The resistance?

PUZZLE

Suppose you placed one probe at the end of the cylinder, and the other at the halfway mark. What should the voltage be now? Make a prediction and test. What does this imply about the resistance of one half of the cylinder? Is this what you expect?

Next, you should try some other measurements:

PREDICTION

If you roll the cylinder into a longer, skinnier cylinder, how should the resistance change? Predict and test.

PREDICTION

If you compress the cylinder into a short, fat cylinder, how should the resistance change? Predict and test.

Next, roll your Play-Doh into a medium length and thickness cylinder. Measure the dimensions. Measure the end-to-end resistance by looking at the voltage and the current as before. Based on these numbers, calculate the resistivity of the sample you are using. You may wish to compare with resistivity values in your text; how does this value compare with numbers for other materials? Is Play-Doh a very good conductor? You should also discuss your numbers with others in your class; you will find that different colors have different resistivities. Can you think of reasons for this? Which color has the lowest resistivity? The highest?

You may also wish to measure the resistance of other shapes. What is the resistance of a sphere? A cube (which is larger: face-to-face resistance, or corner-to-corner)? A torus (doughnut)? Be imaginative!

Please clean up and place the Play-Doh in its sealed container before proceeding to the next part of the lab.

What's in the Box?

You will be provided with a box in which there are four 1kΩ resistors, connected in series and/or in parallel. There are a number of possible combinations; two possible ones are shown below:

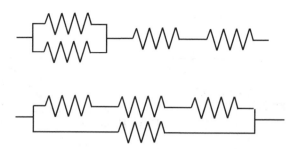

Your mission, should you decide to accept it, is to figure out what is in your box... without opening it up. There are plugs on either side of the box by which you can measure the resistance of the contents. Use your DVM to measure the resistance. Now, figure out how you can combine 4 1kΩ resistors to make this value of resistance. There might be a few ways that are close. Note: the resistors are only accurate to 5%, so there will be some uncertainty involved; you might not be able to decide between two possible options.

Once you have a good guess as to what is in the box, you can check with your instructor to see what is actually in it. Were you right? If you want another try, trade boxes with another group, or try one of the extra boxes around the room.

Resistance of a Lamp

Connect the lamp (represented by a resistor symbol) in a circuit with meters to measure current and voltage:

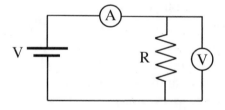

i) Measure the current as a function of applied voltage. Measure enough values to plot a good curve; you may use the computer to plot, should you desire. You will note that the variation is not a straight line. The resistance at any point is defined as V/I; how does this vary as a function of voltage across the bulb? Does it go up or down?

ii) Next, recall: the resistance of the lamp filament is proportional to the temperature. Put a very small voltage across the bulb (the smallest that the supply will provide that still allows you to make a

Figure 3: How to measure the resistance of a Play-Doh cylinder is a fine art, illustrated below.
i) Set up your power supply, DVM (used as an ammeter), brass electrodes, and two Play-Doh electrodes as in below. When something is connected across the gap, current will flow.

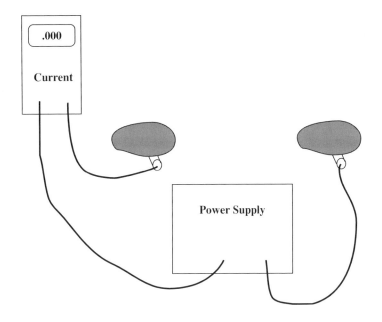

ii) Now, make a nice cylinder of Play-Doh, and connect it up as below. Current flows, as noted.
iii) Now use your voltmeter, with the probes provided (not just the ends of wires!) to measure the voltage across just the piece of Play-Doh that you are looking at.
iv) The ratio of the voltage to the current should be the resistance.

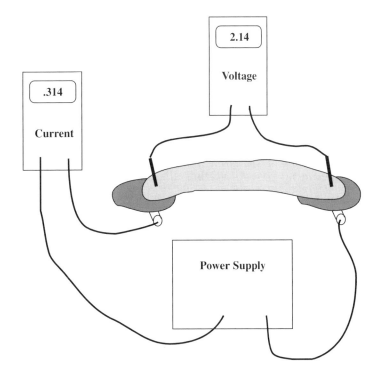

reading), and measure the current. Calculate the resistance; assume that the temperature is room temperature. Now crank up the voltage; measure current and voltage for a large voltage, when the bulb is shining brightly.

PUZZLE

Given the new resistance and your previous measurement, what can you estimate the temperature of the filament to be?

The crucial part of this measurement is making sure that the first measurement is made at very small voltage and current; otherwise, the filament will heat up to well above room temperature. You can put a resistor in series with the bulb to limit the current; this might help.

Summary

In this lab you will have had the chance to do some open-ended investigations of the resistance of different objects: clay, combinations of resistors, and a light bulb. There may well be more to do than you can finish; as usual, this is fine. Just do what you can in the available time. Pick the investigations that seem the most useful to you.

An understanding of resistance and DC circuits is a first step to beginning to understand electronics. Now we are surrounded with electronic devices; it is difficult to imagine that the first electrical device to be in common use, the light bulb, has been around not much over 100 years. The reception that it got on its introduction was mixed; for instance, a committee of the British Parliament reported in 1878 that:

"Edison's work is good enough for our transatlantic friends, but unworthy of the attention of practical or scientific men."

The telephone, which was patented by Bell in 1876, received a similar reception. Previously, in 1865, Joshua Coopersmith was arrested for fraud for trying to raise funds to develop a telephone. An editorial in the Boston Post stated that:

"Well-informed people know it is impossible to transmit the voice over wires and that were it possible to do so, the thing would be of no practical value."

It is remarkable to see the changes that one century has brought about. It makes one wonder what the next will bring. One thing is certain, though: an understanding of Ohm's Law is a good start in getting ready for it. Aren't you glad we are giving you this chance?

Go in peace.

Figure 4: "Bobby," his mother said, "Someday there will be devices to project pictures and sound all over the world. Famous people will tell us stories, and tell us the news. And you, why you might even be a game show host!"

Biological Sensors

Electricity in the Body

Opening Remarks

"Damn it, Jim, I'm a doctor, not an engineer."

- Doctor McCoy, from the old *Star Trek* series

As our technology gets more and more sophisticated, most of us know less and less about how it works; this becomes the realm of specialists and engineers. This is often true of medical practitioners. I once went in for a series of x-rays and was told by the person who was getting me ready for the procedure that the x-ray dose would be "no more than I would get from a day at the beach." This is worrying. I don't know what kind of beach this person goes to, but the ones that I go to involve sunshine, which contains ultraviolet rays - but no x-rays. An understanding of the rudiments of ionizing radiation should be, I would think, a good thing to have before exposing patients to such radiation.

In today's lab you will get a chance to work with two different sensors that are used to collect clinical data on patients. The emphasis is on the physics - not on the biology - so that you might have a better appreciation for how the devices work. This might come in handy if you ever need to use such devices - or have them used on you.

Necessary Theory

Disclaimers

I am a physicist, not a doctor. And no one in your lab is a doctor, either. You are going to use some tools that we provide to take some measurements on your body. All we will guarantee is this: the measurements that you will be asked to make are safe. You will not be injured using the equipment. But we make no claim that what you measure tells you anything at all about any health problems you might have. If the readings you get are screwy, it is most likely your readings that are at fault, not your body. If you have heart problems, PH 122 lab is not the place to diagnose them. Don't use the information you obtain as the basis for any health decisions.

Heart Rate Monitor

When your heart pumps blood into the rest of your body, the blood that comes in is different in one key way from the blood that was there before: it contains more oxygen. When oxygen binds to hemoglobin in your red blood cells, it changes the color of your blood - it makes it more red. This being the case, it is also true that the fresh blood will transmit less red light than the bluer blood that it replaced.

The heart rate monitor that you will use in lab uses this property of your blood to measure your pulse. The device consists of a little clip that goes over

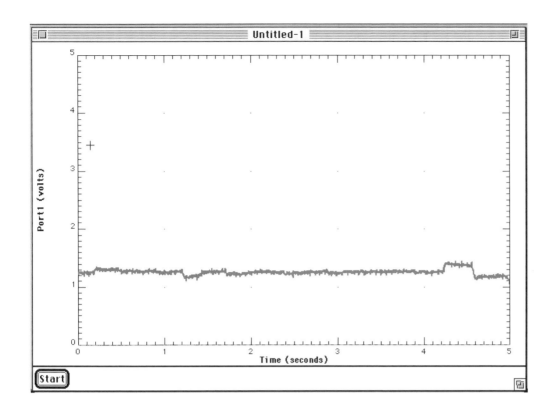

Figure 1: When the electrodes were connected up to the head of a Physics instructor, this was the result. (This looks like a joke, but it is not. Can you see why?)

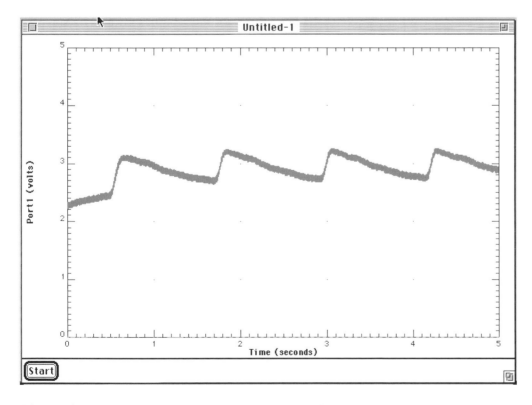

Figure 3: Typical data for the Heart Rate Monitor, with unit clipped to index finger of resting sub-

a finger or perhaps an ear lobe - or even a toe. On one side of the clip is a light; on the other is a light sensor. The sensor measures the light that is transmitted through your finger. There is always a fair amount of light transmitted through you - a lot of the tissues that make up your body are less than totally opaque. But when the new, red blood arrives in your finger from your heart, more of the light will be absorbed in your finger, and less will be transmitted. This will give a dip in the light transmission.

By looking at the time between successive dips, you can determine your pulse. In fact, that is what the unit was designed to do. But it can do more: since the computer will measure the light intensity as a function of time, you can look at how it varies. In particular, you can do the following:

i) Determine the exact instant when the new, fresh blood reaches your finger. If you use the heart rate monitor at the same time as you use the electrocardiogram sensor (which measures when your heart beats) you can determine how long it took the blood to get from your heart to where the sensor is. Does it take longer to get to your ear lobe or your finger?

ii) Look at how the transmission of light varies as a function of time - the light intensity will go back to its former level as the oxygen in your blood is used up. What happens to the graph if you hold your breath?

Note that a higher value on the sensor means less transmission. So, in Figure 2, the graph rises quickly (fresh blood arrives) and then falls slowly (as the oxygen in the blood is used up.)

Electrocardiogram

An electrocardiogram is a set of measures of voltages across a person's body while they are at rest. Muscles in the body work by moving ions across the cell membranes. When any muscle in the body contracts, it produces an electric field. After the contraction, as the ions move back, there will also be a complementary field. (These two phases are called "depolarization" and "repolarization.") You can measure the electric field produced by any muscle in your body, but the muscle that gen-

erally gives the strongest signal is - no surprise - your heart. It turns out that nerve cells produce electric fields too, but these are much weaker. So to make an electroencephalogram - a measure of the voltages between electrodes on the head - you must use a much more sensitive instrument than for an electrocardiogram, or ECG.

When your heart beats, it produces a dipole electric field in your chest cavity that will produce measurable voltages across the body. Electrodes connected to the body can measure these voltages, and can give a good indication of exactly what the heart is up to - from basic information such as how fast it is beating to more detailed information such as the presence of certain arrhythmias.

A basic ECG as measured by the equipment you will use in the lab appears as in Figure 4. There are a number of different peaks, but the strongest - the sharp vertical spikes - are from the ventricles. This peak (called the "R" peak in an ECG) corresponds to a field across the heart as shown in Figure 3. Exactly why this is so depends on details of cardiac physiology, but for our purposes note this: this electric field can be deduced by measuring the voltage difference between pairs of points on the body. In the lab, you will connect up electrodes to a person's body and measure voltage differences between the electrodes. There are a few things to note:

i) What you really want to measure is the voltage across the chest cavity, but the arms and legs can be viewed as equipotentials. So instead of using the electrodes to measure the voltage between, say, a person's left shoulder and their right hip, you can measure the voltage between their left wrist and their right ankle - a much easier and less embarrassing proposition.

ii) There are three electrodes on our ECG device. The voltage displayed will be the voltage between the red electrode and the green electrode; the black electrode serves to eliminate noise. (A person is a pretty good radio antenna, and so will pick up all sorts of interference. The black electrode essentially serves to ground the person out so that this interference is minimized.)

iii) The voltage that you measure on the ECG will

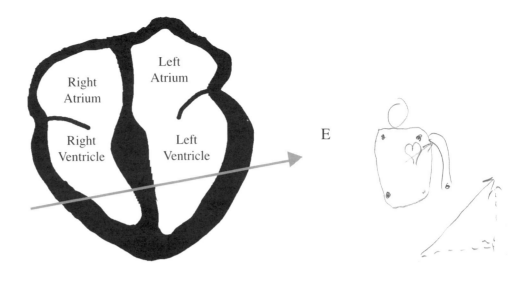

Figure 3: There are a number of different electrical signals from your heart, but the biggest signal comes from your ventricles (no surprise, really, as they are larger than the atriums.) The big peak (the "R" peak, in the language of ECGs) of the record of Figure 4 corresponds to an electric field across the heart (and the chest cavity) directed as above.

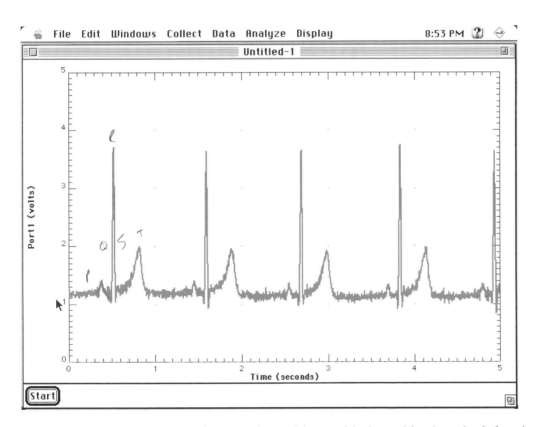

Figure 4: Typical ECG data for a resting subject, with the red lead on the left wrist, the green lead on the right wrist, and the black lead on the right ankle.

depend on where the electrodes are placed. For instance, look at the trace in Figure 4: the red electrode was on the left wrist and the green electrode on the right wrist, giving the trace shown. If the red and green electrodes were reversed, you would expect that the trace would be inverted - the sign of the voltages would be switched.

The fact that you can place the electrodes in different positions will lead the most interesting part of the lab: determining how a person's heart is situated in their chest cavity. If you situate the electrodes so that the "R" peak vanishes, the electrodes must be on an equipotential - meaning that a line between them must be perpendicular to the electric field! Think about what you have learned about equipotentials and fields.

Experiments and Calculations

Equipment Needed

Each lab group will get one set of the following ECG equipment:

> Vernier ECG unit

and a set of pulse measurement equipment:

> Vernier Heart Rate Monitor

Each of these pieces of equipment is connected to an interface box that is used with the computer:

> Vernier Universal Lab Interface
> Macintosh computer

The software that is used to run the interface is called Data Logger; it looks a lot like the motion software that was used in the PH 121/141 course.

The electrodes for the ECG unit will attach to little pads that are stuck to the skin. We will have a limited number of these pads for each lab group; think carefully about how to use them!

Health and Safety Concerns

There is one key piece of safety information here: when you have electrodes hooked up to your body, DON'T HOOK THEM UP TO ANYTHING EXCEPT FOR THE WIRES OF THE ECG DEVICE! There is a very good reason for this. The point of the electrodes is to make very good electrical contact with your skin. This being true, if you were to connect them to, say, a power supply, you could be in serious danger of physical harm. The ECG device has several safety features built into it that will keep it from being able to put a dangerous voltage across you - so you can hook these wires to the electrodes with no worries.

The electrodes, after you pull them off of your skin, should be disposed of as you would old bandages. You can reuse them on yourself, but don't share them with others.

The pulse sensor will be clipped over the end of a finger (or perhaps a toe.) There is no real risk of disease transmission here, but we will ask you to wipe off the sensor once you are through with it.

And, once again - don't use any information you acquire in lab to assess your medical state.

Heart Rate Monitor

Inspect the Heart Rate Monitor to see how it works: it consists of a little light source and a light sensor, with your finger (or other body part) clipped in between.

Your body, though you may not think of it, will actually transmit some light. Light that shines through your flesh tends to be quite reddened - due to the red color of your blood. And when the blood is fresh from your heart, with lots of oxygen, it is quite a bit redder. If you clip the monitor over your finger, every time fresh blood comes into your finger the light that shines through your finger will be reduced. As the oxygen in the blood is used up, more light will be passed. When your heart pumps in more fresh blood, the cycle starts again.

Pick someone from the group to be a test subject, and clip the Heart Rate Monitor over their finger. He or she should sit very, very still with his or her hand resting on the table. Open up the appropriate software package to collect data from the unit, and click on the button that says "Start." You will get several seconds of data from the unit. If things are working well, it will look something like Figure 2.

Notice that the sensor works backwards from how you might think: when your heart beats, less light is transmitted, but the voltage reading *increases* - it makes a little bump. This is a function of the circuit used to make the measurements, but there is a good reason for letting it stay this way: a pulse looks like a bump, not a dip. This is more comforting to people, so the folks who make the unit let it stay this way.

Get a good set of data that you can trust, and consider the following questions:

QUESTION

What is the pulse rate of the person that you took data on? How do you determine this? Does this rate stay constant, or does it vary? How could you tell?

QUESTION

Why does the trace go up quickly, but then drop slowly?

QUESTION

What sort of things would cause errors in the readings? Why is it important to stay still? Since the sensor measures light, do the room lights make a difference? Do you get better readings with the lights off?

It is also worth considering why the unit is clipped to your finger. Pick another test subject, and try the following:

• Get a good sample with the sensor clipped to the subject's finger.

• Get a good sample with the sensor clipped to the subject's ear lobe or toe.

QUESTION

How do the readings differ in the second case? Why would this be so? Use what you

know about blood flow in the body.

Finally, try one more experiment:

Pick another test subject, and have them get a reading with the unit connected to their finger. Now have them hold their breath for a long time, and see how the readings change. Then let them breathe again.

QUESTION

How does all of this affect the readings? Can you explain what is going on?

Other Things to Try

If you have time and interest, you might also want to use the unit to measure other things: change in the data after vigorous exercise, for instance. Your instructor will have other suggestions.

Straight from the Heart: ECG Measurements

You will be given a limited number of electrodes for this part of the experiment. There should be enough to make measurements on every member of your group - if you are careful with them.

The electrodes need to make very good contact with the skin for best results. If you are the test subject, once you figure out where you wish to put the electrodes, you should wash and dry the place where the electrodes will go. (Drying is very important! The electrodes will not stick to moist skin.)

It is easiest to attach the electrodes to your extremities - to your left or right wrist, or your ankles. The voltage at your left wrist is approximately equal to the voltage from your left shoulder - as far as the signal from your heart is concerned. So you need not connect electrodes to your chest, thighs, and so on - wrists and ankles will suffice. (Unless you want to measure voltages front to back across your chest - which you may well want to do.)

First Steps

For your first measurement, pick a test subject, and have them connect electrodes to their right and left

69

wrists, and to their right ankle. Connect the wires as follows:

- Red wire to left wrist
- Green wire to right wrist

Leave the black wire disconnected for now. Start up the software, and begin collecting data. You should get a trace that has very little useful information. The black wire is the ground wire, and it is a very important part of the system! Even though it is not being used to collect data, it is crucial that it be connected.

Finish connecting your test subject by making the connection:

- Black wire to right ankle

Have the test subject sit quietly, start the software, and obtain a good trace. You should get something like the diagram in Figure 4.

QUESTION

The big peaks are from the ventricles - the spike and the following bump. Can you see corresponding features for the atriums? Why are these so much smaller?

Other Muscles

Your heart is not the only muscle in your body which makes electrical signals - it just makes them all the time. Pick a test subject put on electrodes and connect wires to their body as follows:

- Red wire to upper left arm
- Green wire to left wrist
- Black wire to right ankle

Given what you know about how this device works, predict what sort of trace you will see now:

PREDICTION

When you take data with the wires connected like so, and the subject at rest, what sort of trace should you see?

Now take a trace, and see what you get. How does this differ from the previous result? Why?

Next, have the subject flex the muscles in their left

arm, and take data again. What do you see this time? Explain what you are seeing.

Other Axes

Pick a test subject, and have them put electrodes on their left and right wrists and their right ankle. Have them connect the electrodes as follows:

- Red wire to left wrist
- Green wire to right wrist
- Black wire to right ankle

Take a trace, and print out what you get so that you can refer to it later.

Next, have the test subject leave the electrodes in place, but reconnect the wires as follows:

- Red wire to left wrist
- Black wire to right wrist
- Green wire to right ankle

This will take a voltage across the body in a different direction. Take a trace, and compare it to what you saw before. How does it differ? Print out a copy, and try another connection:

- Black wire to left wrist
- Red wire to right wrist
- Green wire to right ankle

This is a slightly different axis than before. Take a trace, and compare it to the two previous cases. How do the results differ?

Folks who do these measurements for a living connect up a bunch of electrodes, and look at different combinations of electrodes - known as leads - to give them different information about the heart. Do you see any features in one wire arrangement that are more clear than in the other arrangements?

Orientation of your Heart

There are other electrode positions you could try. You might try one right over the heart, or on the neck, with wrist or leg electrodes. How about an electrode on the chest and one on the back - to give a front-to-back reading. Think about other axes that you can measure.

In each of these cases, as well as the previous cases,

you are measuring the voltage between the red and green electrodes - and so the voltage difference along a line connecting the two electrodes. If the "R" peak is large, the line connecting the electrodes is nearly parallel to the electric field of your heart as shown in Figure 3. If the "R" peak is small, the line connecting the electrodes is nearly perpendicular to the electric field of your heart.

PUZZLE

By looking at the traces for different electrode placements, it is possible to determine the orientation of your heart in your chest cavity. Think about how to do this, take some traces, and see what you can deduce from your results. Note: your heart might be rotated in your chest; you need to consider this too! If you put the red electrode on your chest and the green electrode on your back, think about the signal you will get. This is an interesting puzzle; pick a member of your group who doesn't mind having electrodes stuck to them, and see if you can figure out how their heart is oriented in their chest.

Other Things to Try

There are other things that you could look at:

• How does a person's ECG vary before and after vigorous exercise?

• How does a person's ECG vary with body position? Does lying down make for a different trace than standing up?

Grand Finale: Putting it All Together

Next, hook up a person to both the ECG and the heart rate monitor, and display both traces at the same time. Look at the traces that you get, and consider:

PUZZLE

How long does it take for the blood to get from the heart to a finger? How about to an earlobe? A toe?

Think about how to measure this, and see what you get. Does it make a difference if the finger is raised up over a person's head, or if it is lowered to their side?

What other measurements could you make with both devices working together? Think about the possibilities, and, if you have time, try something out.

Summing Up

In the course of my career, I have, on more occasions than I care to remember, hooked up a voltmeter or an oscilloscope to a piece of equipment to diagnose what is wrong with it. It was a very interesting exercise for me to hook up what is essentially a fancy voltmeter to my body, and measure what was going on inside it. Our tools, when used correctly, allow us to see farther and deeper, and this knowledge is very empowering. But I must say that I got more of a kick out of measuring just how my heart is tilted in my chest than I ever did hooking up a voltmeter to a piece of lab equipment.

Go in peace.

RC Circuits

The Mathematics of Decay

Opening Remarks

In your studies of capacitors, you saw that the voltage on a capacitor was proportional to the charge stored in it. (Surely you haven't forgotten this already!) In this lab, we use a capacitor as a circuit device, specifically a device with this useful ability to store charge. When a capacitor is charged up, then connected in series with a resistor, the capacitor will drive a current through the resistor and thus discharge. As the capacitor discharges, its voltage drops. This in turn will mean a decrease in the *rate* of discharge. The lower the voltage falls, the slower any further decrease. The voltage thus drops to zero in an asymptotic sense, sort of sidling up to it, in a rather coy fashion. This is illustrated in Figure 1; note the definition of the time constant.

Capacitors are similarly coy about charging up; look at Figure 2. The voltage asymptotically approaches the charging voltage; we can define a time constant for this in a similar sense to the previous case.

In this lab, we will look at circuits in which capacitors are charging and discharging. The basic RC circuits that we will study are an interesting case of time-dependent circuits; actually, such circuits can be and are used in simple timers. You will see some unintentional examples in the lab. For instance, some power supplies will keep their indicator light lit for some time after the switch is turned off. One type you will see doesn't produce

voltage until it has been switched on for a few seconds. These are cases of capacitors discharging and charging, respectively.

We will use the computer to measure the voltages produced in the circuits, so we can plot them as a function of time and perform some simple analyses. Enjoy!

Necessary Theory

"I only wish he would explain his explanation."

- Lord Byron

Exponential Decay

Consider the simplest series RC circuit:

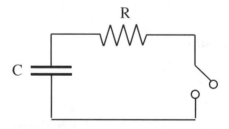

The capacitor is initially charged to a voltage V_o. At time $t = 0$ the switch is closed and current begins to flow. The capacitor discharges, and the voltage decreases.

As noted above, as the voltage decreases, the current will also decrease. Thus, the *rate* at which the capacitor discharges will also decrease. If we plot the voltage as a function of time, we can see this

72

Figure 1: Voltage vs. time for a capacitor discharging through a resistor. Note the graphical meaning of the time constant $\tau = RC$. In this case, the time constant is 1.0 seconds.

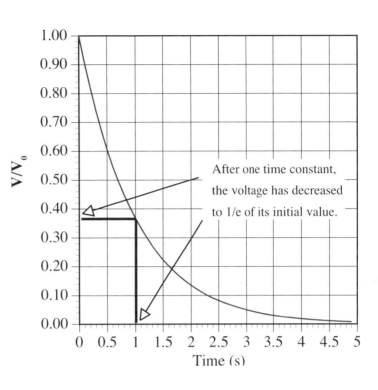

After one time constant, the voltage has decreased to 1/e of its initial value.

Figure 2: Voltage vs. time for a capacitor charging through a resistor. Note the graphical meaning of the time constant $\tau = RC$.

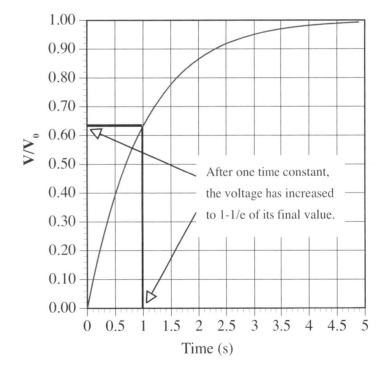

After one time constant, the voltage has increased to 1-1/e of its final value.

73

- the graph gets flatter and flatter as time goes on; see Figure 1. This kind of graph is associated with systems where the rate of decrease of a quantity is proportional to the quantity itself, which is known as exponential decay.

The reason for this name is clear from the equation governing the decrease in the voltage:

$$V = V_0 e^{-t/RC}$$

In this equation, V_0 is the initial voltage, and V is the voltage at a time t. This voltage is always less than V_0. Note that for the decay, what is important is the *product* of the resistance and the capacitance. This combination, RC, has the units of seconds and is known as the time constant.

The meaning of the time constant is illustrated in the graph in Figure 1. Note that at a time t = RC the voltage has decreased to 1/e, or 36.8%, of its initial value. You can see this by looking at the equation: at time t = RC,

$$V = V_0 e^{-RC/RC} = V_0 e^{-1} = V_0/e$$

So the time constant is the time required for the voltage to decrease to 36.8% of its initial value. You may be familiar with the idea of a half-life: a radioactive source will decay to 50% of its initial strength in one half-life. This is another example of an exponential decay. In the case of an RC circuit, think of the time constant as a "1/e life." As a matter of fact, you can define a half-life for the system; it is just the time constant multiplied by ln(2).

Charging a Capacitor: Not for the Zeno-Phobe

It is also useful to consider circuits in which capacitors are charging and not discharging, such as the following one:

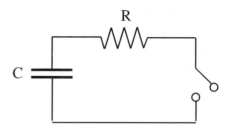

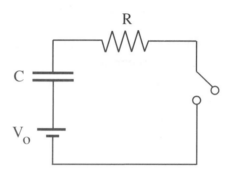

The capacitor is initially uncharged, and the switch is closed at time t = 0. In this case, the voltage increases with time. The graph illustrating the voltage vs. time is in Figure 2. Notice the new meaning of the time constant - the time for the voltage to increase to (1-1/e) of its final value. The equation for this process is as follows:

$$V = V_0(1-e^{-t/RC})$$

Compare this with the previous equation.

The above equation describes the charging of a capacitor. Notice that it never gets to a voltage V_0. It gets as close as we want, but it never gets there. This is reminiscent of the paradox of Zeno. Zeno argued that space was not infinitely divisible. Consider someone walking toward a wall. First she must cover half of the distance to the wall. Then, she must cover half of the remaining distance. There is still some distance remaining, so she covers half of this.... And so on. Zeno argued that the process had to break down, or else it would take an infinite amount of time to get to the wall—and of course, it doesn't. Can you see the flaw in his argument?

At any rate, in the case of the capacitor, after several dozen time constants the difference between the voltage and the charging voltage will be less than the voltage added by one more electron, so we might as well say it is fully charged up. Since charge is quantized, the process does break down—so for this case, Zeno was right.

Self-Similarity

The graph of exponential decay presented above has an interesting feature: its shape stays constant. If you take off the first part of the graph, and expand the remainder so that it fills the scale, the result will be a graph that looks like the original. No matter what scale you look at the graph on, the shape is the same; this is a property known as self-similarity.

As you are taking your data on the computer, it will be an easy matter for you to re-scale the graph that you obtain and check this out. This is illustrated in Figure 4. You should make a point of trying this.

Experiments and Calculations

Necessary Equipment

The apparatus that you will need for the experiment is as follows:

> Mac, interface, Data Logger program
> 5V fixed power supply
> single pole double throw switch
> component board with resistor, capacitor
> 1F capacitor and light bulb

The interface that we will be using comes with probes to directly measure voltages. These probes have clip leads that are designed to hook onto the leads of components or bare wires. Do not clip them onto a socket or a plug. You will be using the interface with the Data Logger program that you have used previously.

The 5 V fixed power supply puts out only exactly 5 V. This is full scale for measurements on the interface board. The interface can't measure negative voltages, so be sure that the power supply and the probes are connected with the proper polarity. If you suspect that you are not sure about polarities, ask before turning anything on!

The capacitors and resistors that you use will be on a board, with plugs for making connections.

Your TA will have information about the values of the resistors and capacitors. The 1 F capacitor is for later!

Measuring Decay

Build the first circuit in Figure 3. When the capacitor is connected to the power supply, it will charge up. When it is then switched to the resistor, it will discharge. We are interested in the voltage across the capacitor, so connect the leads from your interface to the capacitor.

Start the program from the stack or by clicking on the appropriate icon. The program should start up with reasonable values for this case, but you should feel free to change them.

Set the interface to begin collecting data, with a long collection time. The capacitor should initially be uncharged, so you should be measuring 0 V. Now connect the capacitor to the power supply by throwing the switch. You should see the measured voltage jump to 5 V; if you don't, something is wrong.

Next, throw the switch to connect the capacitor across the resistor, and observe the decay in voltage. You may wish to try this a few times to get a good set of data on a good time scale. When you have some data that is worth working with, consider:

• From your graph, what is the time constant for the RC circuit you have just measured?

• Compare your measured time constant with the value you predict using the nominal values of the resistor and capacitor. (Information on how to read the resistor and capacitor values will be provided.)

• If you expand your graph as noted in Figure 4 and discussed above, do you see that the expanded graph has the same shape as the original? Try measuring a time constant off the expanded graph; do you get the same result?

Before taking additional measurements, move the data you have taken into Data B (an option under the "Data" menu), so that additional data that you take can be easily compared with it.

Now, leave the circuit the same, but connect the leads across the resistor, noting the correct polarity. You will be measuring the voltage across the resistor, which will be proportional to the current in the circuit.

PREDICTION

Given what you have measured for the capacitor, what do you predict for the voltage across the resistor as a function of time? Make a sketch that you can compare against before you take any data. Be quantitative—draw a sketch with numbers of the axes.

Once you and your lab partners have made a prediction, test this prediction by running the experiment. Charge the capacitor up as before, then measure the voltage across the resistor as it discharges. Does what you observe agree with your prediction?

Here are two more activities that you might try while your circuit is still set up this way. Move the voltage probe back to the capacitor and:

i) Charge your capacitor up, then put the switch to the middle, where the capacitor is disconnected. The capacitor is now connected only to the probes of the interface. Nonetheless, the measurement unit has a certain associated resistance, and so the capacitor will slowly discharge. Set the time scale for a very long value; can you see the decay? If it seems practical, measure a long enough time to give you a decent measurement of the time constant. What does the measured time constant give as a value of the resistance of the probes? (Note: this might be a practical technique for measuring large resistances, which will be out of the range of a typical DVM.)

ii) When you are charging the capacitor up, can you see a charging curve? The power supply has a (small) internal resistance, so there will be some (small) time constant for the charging. Can you measure it?

Measuring Charging

Next, connect the circuit as shown in the second diagram in Figure 3. Connect the leads across the capacitor. Short the capacitor out to be sure that it is discharged, and take data on the charging curve as you did for the discharge. Try it a few times to get some data you are happy with, then consider:

• What is the measured time constant? Does it agree with the value you measured before?

• How long does it take for the capacitor to charge up to a point where you can detect no further change in voltage?

Before you continue, move the data you have taken to your second data register.

Next, connect the probes across the resistor, and, before you take any data:

PREDICTION

Predict what curve you should measure for the voltage across the resistor as a function of time. Make a sketch that you can compare with later.

Once you and your partners have settled on a prediction, test it. Is your prediction verified? Compare the data you saved previously with the data you have just taken. Discuss what is happening at different times on the graph.

A Blast from the Past

The 1 F capacitors and the bulbs that you used in a previous experiment will also be available. Charge up a capacitor and discharge it through a bulb. Measure the voltage across the capacitor. When you measure the decay, it will not be exactly exponential (how can you check this?); why is this? Think about the resistance of the light bulb as the experiment goes on. (Note: in this section of the experiment, it is crucial that you connect the capacitor the right way around!)

You might also look for a charging curve as you did in the previous case; it takes some time for the power supplies to get the 1 F capacitors up to full charge!

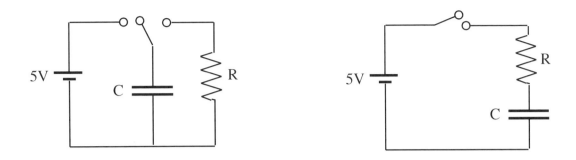

Figure 3: Circuits needed for the first and second parts of the experiment, respectively.

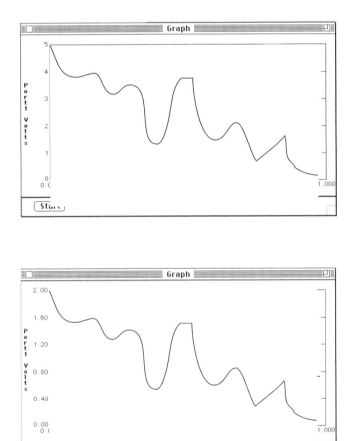

Figure 4: V vs. t data will be displayed in the graph window. A portion of the graph can be expanded by dragging a rectangle with the mouse while holding down the command key; the section selected will be expanded. Expanding the tail end of the curve, as shown, may be of interest - as described in

Summing Up

"Population, when unchecked, increases in a geometrical ratio. Subsistence increases only in an arithmetical ratio. A slight acquaintance with numbers will show the immensity of the first power in comparison with the second."

- Thomas Robert Malthus, *An Essay on the Principle of Population*

A charged capacitor, connected in series with a resistor, will discharge through it. The rate of discharge is given by the current; the current is determined by the voltage. As the voltage decreases, so does the current. Thus, as the voltage decreases, so does its *rate* of decrease; the net result is a gradual decrease of voltage as we have seen. The kind of decay curve shown is called exponential decay; it is typified by a half life. If the voltage starts at 1 volt and drops to 1/2 volt in 1 second, it will drop by another factor of 2 in the next second: at 2 seconds, the voltage will be 1/4 volt. At 3 seconds, it will be 1/8 volt, at 4 seconds 1/16 volt, and so on. Each second will see another halving of the voltage.

The flip side to exponential decay is exponential growth. Whereas in exponential decay a value drops by a factor of two each half life, in exponential growth a value doubles each doubling time. This is the sort of mathematics that typifies population growth: the rate of increase of the population is proportional to the number of people, so the larger the population the faster the increase. There is a present-day country, about the size of Massachusetts, whose population doubles every 20 years, and has for quite some time; this is not an unusual growth rate for parts of the world. This country at present has a population of 750,000. In 20 years it will be 1,500,000. In 40 years, it will be 3,000,000, should the trend continue. In 200 years, if the growth continued unchecked, this country would have 768,000,000 people - or about triple the current population of the United States, packed into a Massachusetts-size area. Oh, and just out of interest, we can calculate that in 500 years this country would have 25,165,824,000,000,000 people - i.e. a little more than 25 quadrillion. At this point, there will not be room enough for everyone to stand; my conservative calculation puts people stacked 20 deep, border to border. 420 years later, they would form a column stacked all the way to the moon. You can do similar calculations for many of the world's countries; clearly, something must give.

The principles of exponential growth and decay are pervasive in science. Let us hope that it does not take us another 200 years to learn the lesson of exponential growth, and apply it to our numbers.

Go in peace.

Figure 5: A classic puzzler: water lilies are growing on a pond. Each day, they double the area of the pond that they cover. This goes on for 30 days. On the 30th day, the pond is totally covered. On what day was the pond 1/2 covered? The answer: on the 29th day. This is the problem with exponential growth: the limits sort of sneak up on you. And this is why so many people have difficulty assimilating its lessons.

Figure 6: The PH 142 lab manual doubled in size over a three year period. If this trend were to continue, some time after 2050 the height of the manual would for the first time exceed the diameter of the earth. This would be a momentous time, though it would necessitate some redesign of the Physics labs.

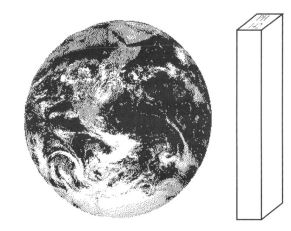

Cathode Rays

Observing the Path of an Electron Beam

Opening Remarks

Homage to the Chinese Master, Bo Ling:

Fingers dipping like rat fangs
into the round black cheese
— O moon that orbits Milwaukee —
you heave it onto the path,
the wayless Way,
the long and slippery road
at whose end there await,
amidst thunder,
the ten Buddhas.

- Tom Robbins, *Half Asleep in Frog Pajamas*

In televisions, computer monitors, and oscilloscopes, an electron beam (or cathode rays, as they were called historically) launched from the back of the tube travels through the airless interior until it hits the screen at the front of the tube. The screen is coated on the inside with phosphors that glow when electrically excited by the beam. Along the way, the beam is deflected by electric or magnetic fields that are used to move the beam back and forth across the screen, drawing the picture that you see.

In lab today, you will use a sort of naked cathode ray tube. Electrons are freed from a hot filament in the back of the tube. You will apply an accelerating voltage to pull the electrons away and accelerate them down the tube. If you do nothing else, the beam of electrons will hit the front of the tube, the screen, and make a glowing spot where they hit the

phosphor. Of course, we won't leave it here; we will deflect the beam. As in bowling, we will seek to master the curve, the forces that cause the beam to leave its path, to better understand them.

Necessary Theory

Note: There are certain calculations in this section that you should do and put in a report along with measurements and observations.

Forces on Electrons

In a cathode ray tube, the first thing that is done is that electrons from a hot filament (emitted by a process called *thermionic emission*) are accelerated. Suppose you put a plate with a hole in it in front of the filament, and put a voltage on the plate so that it was at a positive voltage with respect to the filament; see Figure 2. There would be an electric field as shown, and this would accelerate the electrons to the left. Some of the electrons would go through the hole and continue on — an electron beam. Something like this happens inside the tube that you will use; you will apply the accelerating voltage, and so you will determine how fast the electrons in the beam are moving. Since the electron is so light, even a modest acceleration gets it up to a pretty darn good speed.

A beam of electrons can be deflected in two different ways:

• By an electric field. There will be two pairs of

80

Figure 1: Whether you like it or not, you probably spend a fair amount of time every day watching images projected on screens by cathode rays. You know how certain of the cognescenti call computer monitors "CRTs"? That stands for **c**athode **r**ay **t**ube, which is just what the monitor is: a beam of electrons (cathode rays) is swept across the screen to draw the pattern that you see. TVs work the same way. There are many consequences of this fact:

• The screen flickers, as the beam can't be everywhere at once. Think about when you have seen computer monitors on TV - they flicker strangely, don't they? The image on the screen is drawn, fades, and then is redrawn. Shake your hand in front of a monitor; what do you see? See the Little Shop of Physics Web site for other ideas along this line (http://www.littleshop.physics.colostate.edu).

• A static charge builds up on the screen. That's why computer and television screens get so dusty!

• A magnet brought near the screen will deflect the electron beam, and so will distort the picture on the monitor. If you put a magnet right on the screen of a color TV or monitor, it can magnetize the shadow mask behind the glass (it's made of iron), and so some of the distortion will persist. You can fix this; most monitors these days have "degaussing" circuits built into them which demagnetize the screen. And if you do it to a TV, you can demagnetize them, too. Ask if you want more details. Here's a question for you: why don't static charges—with the accompanying electric fields—affect the picture? Give this some thought!

---

plates inside the tube; the beam will go through the gaps in the plates (see Figure 2). If you apply a voltage to the plates, there will be an electric field between them, and this will deflect the beam.

• By a magnetic field. You will use magnets and a solenoid to bring a magnetic field into the region of the beam. This will also deflect the beam.

More details will be provided in the following sections, where you will get a chance to explore the effects of both electric and magnetic fields on the beam.

Experiments and Calculations

Equipment Needed

Each group will be provided with the following equipment:

> CRT device in cradle
> Multiple power supply for filament and
>   accelerating voltage
> High voltage power supply for deflecting
>   beam
> Bar magnet
> Solenoid to put around CRT

There are two main points to be aware of:

• The CRT device can be damaged if electrical connections are incorrect. You will be given explicit instructions as to how to use the device by your instructor; do not turn it on or make any adjustments until you have been shown how to work with it!

• There are high voltage sources used in this experiment that will hurt if you touch them. I suggest that you don't touch them.

Accelerating the Beam

The electrical connections to the tube will already be made; carefully note where the power supply is that provides current to the filament (6.3 V AC, not to be adjusted!) and where the power supply is that provides the voltage to accelerate the beam (0-400 V, which you can adjust.) Turn on the supply to the filament, and then set the accelerating voltage to 200 V. After some time, you should see a spot appear on the front of the screen.

When an electron (charge e) is accelerated through a voltage V_a, it gains an amount of kinetic energy given by the following expression:

$$\text{KE of electron} = eV_a = \tfrac{1}{2}mv^2$$

We know what the kinetic energy of a moving object is in terms of its mass and its velocity.

DERIVATION

Write down an expression for the kinetic energy of the electron, and equate it to the above expression. Solve for the velocity of the electron in terms of other quantities.

QUESTION

When you accelerate the electron through a voltage of 400 V (which you will do!); what will be the speed the electron is moving at? What fraction of the speed of light is this? Do we have to worry about relativity here?

Does the appearance of the spot on the front of the screen change if you change the accelerating voltage? Think about what is going on, and comment

.Deflecting the Beam I: Electric Fields

There are two pairs of plates in the back of the tube (as shown in Figure 2) that allow you to put an electric field perpendicular to the beam, thus deflecting it. This is sketched in more detail in Figure 3.

Connect wires to the terminals that allow you to deflect the beam in the X direction, but don't connect them to anything. You should see a line on the screen. Touch the end of one lead, and notice the line now. The lead is picking up stray voltages from the 60 Hz AC power in the room; the resulting electric field on the plates is sweeping the beam back and forth. Cool, isn't it? When you touch the lead, you act as an antenna to make the pickup of the stray fields better. The line on the screen shows you the line along which the beam is deflected when you apply a voltage to the X terminals. Rotate the tube until this line is horizontal.

Take the leads out so that the beam hits the center of the screen, and note the position. (It might not hit the center, as the beam might not be perfectly aligned If it doesn't, just note where it does hit.) Apply a voltage from your low-voltage power supply to the X terminals, and vary it. How does the spot move as you change the voltage? Set the voltage so that the spot is deflected by one centimeter to the side, as noted on the grid with the screen.

QUESTION

If you were to switch the polarity of the leads, how should the position of the spot change? Make a prediction, and test it.

It is also instructive to see how much the beam moves for given voltages.

QUESTION

Set the voltage so that the beam moves by 1 centimeter to the side.

Next, measure what voltage you have to set the dial to so that the beam will move 2 centimeters to the side.

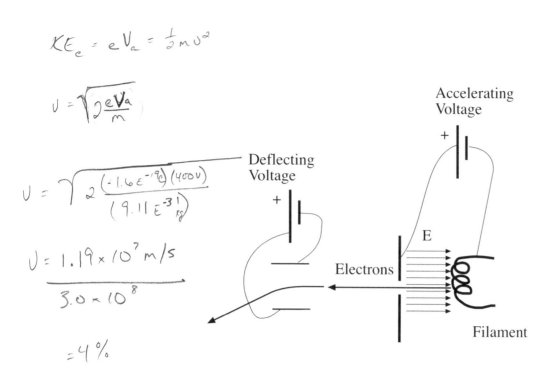

$$KE_e = eV_a = \frac{1}{2}mv^2$$

$$v = \sqrt{\frac{2eV_a}{m}}$$

$$v = \sqrt{2\frac{(-1.6E^{-19})(400v)}{(9.11E^{-31}\frac{1}{kg})}}$$

$$v = 1.19 \times 10^7 \, m/s$$

$$\overline{3.0 \times 10^8}$$

$$= 4\%$$

Figure 2: Electrons from the hot filament are accelerated by the electric field between the filament and a grid. There are other electrodes that focus the beam; these are emitted for clarity. After being accelerated, the beam of electrons is bent by an electric field between two plates, as shown. There is another set of plates at right angles to the first that bends the beam in or out of the page.

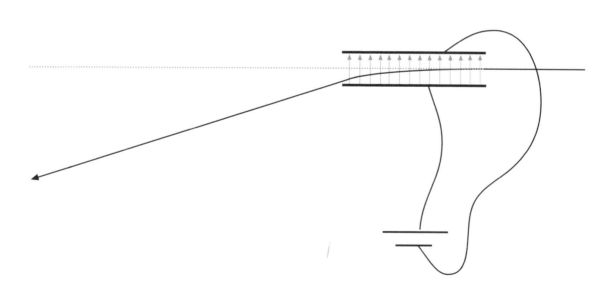

Figure 3: A close-up of the above situation. The beam is deflected in the region between the plates, by the electric field, as shown. The deflection of the beam (by which we mean this: Think about where the beam would have hit, were there no field. How far from here does it hit? That's the deflection) depends on the size of the electric field and the time of flight of the beam (how long it takes it to travel

QUESTION

Explain how this proportionality allows the CRT to be used, essentially, as a voltmeter.

Next, set the beam up so that the spot moves by 1 cm to the side again.

QUESTION

What will happen to the position of the spot if the accelerating voltage is increased? Make a prediction and test. Be sure to thank about and explain what is going on.

Deflecting the Beam II: Magnetic Fields

You have been given a bar magnet to use for this part of the experiment. You will be asked to make some predictions and then to test them. Please make your predictions and record them before you try the experiment!

Set the tube up with the beam hitting the central spot on the screen. Now, take your bar magnet, and use it to deflect the beam. Think about the sense of the force that the magnet makes on the moving charges. For the record, you can assume that the magnetic field lines of the bar magnet come out of the N pole and go into the S pole; near the poles, the field lines will appear as follows:

You can assume, to a good approximation, that the field lines near the end of the magnet are parallel to the bar and directed as shown.

PREDICTION

Suppose you bring the bar magnet up to the side of the tube like so:

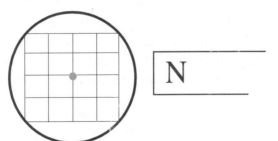

Which way will the spot move? Make a prediction!

Once you have made a prediction, test it out. Did you see what you observed?

PREDICTION

Now, suppose you bring the bar magnet up to the side of the tube in the opposite orientation:

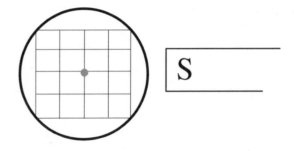

Which way will the spot move? Make a prediction!

Once you have made a prediction, test it out. Did you see what you observed?

Suppose you change the velocity of the beam by increasing the accelerating voltage. How will this change the position of the deflected spot? Will it be deflected by more, less, or the same amount?

QUESTION

Write down an expression for the force on the beam from the magnet. Think about how this varies with the speed of the beam, and think about the time of flight of the beam. How will changing the speed of the beam affect how much the magnetic field deflects the beam?

Now, set up to make a test as follows: put the magnet in a fixed position, set the accelerating voltage to 200 V, and note by how much the beam is deflected. Now increase the accelerating voltage. How does this change the deflection of the beam? Does the change make the difference that you predicted?

Deflecting the Beam III: Magnetic Fields from a Solenoid

Next, place your tube unit inside the solenoid, and connect the solenoid to your low-voltage power supply. Set the accelerating voltage to 200 V, get a nice spot on the screen, and then turn off the focusing so that you get a fuzzy spot on the screen.

Next, turn up the voltage on the solenoid. At some point, you should see that you get a dot on the screen.

QUESTION

Can you see how the focus control on the tube works? Explain in some detail what might be going on.

QUESTION

So why would the magnetic field of the solenoid work this way? Let's do some experiments to test, shall we?

Take the beam and get a nice, focused spot on the screen. Now connect up leads to the X deflection electrodes so that you get a line as before. Now turn up the voltage on the solenoid; what happens to the line? Can you get it back to a spot as before? Where is the spot?

You should see that no matter what the transverse velocity of the electrons (as accelerated through the plates) the electrons eventually end up back where they started! The electrons will spiral around the field line, and will each make a spiral that takes the same amount of time. If they each make a complete circle in the time that the beam takes to get to the screen, each electron will end up back where it started from - and so you will get a spot on the screen.

Think about it; see if you can make a sketch of what is happening.

And One Final Puzzle

This is a complicated problem - but one that you can do, if you have enough time. If you have some time left after completing the above measurements, give it a shot.

When we bought this equipment, it was described as a "Charge of the Electron Apparatus." It purported to allow you to measure the charge on the electron by the following method:

i) Get a nice spot at the center of the screen.

ii) Deflect the beam to the side - either by applying a known voltage or by leaving a lead free as before. (This will give the usual line trace.)

iii) Measuring how much current through the solenoid is necessary to focus the beam back to a spot in the center of the screen.

In principle, this is all you need to do to determine a value for "e." A sketch of the relevant motions of the electron is given in Figure 4.

PUZZLE

As noted in the previous section, if you get the beam back to a spot, the electrons will have traveled in one complete circle. Assume that you have an electron that is accelerated through some known voltage, so that you know its velocity. You also know - or can measure - the length of the tube, from where the electron is accelerated to where it hits the screen. Therefore, you can figure out the electron's time of flight: how long it takes to complete its circular orbit.

Assume some transverse velocity for the electron; just call it v_t or something. It will cancel at some point anyway. Now, if you apply a field parallel to the tube, this transverse velocity will cause the electron to travel in a circular path. Calculate the time for the electron to travel in this circular path; when you do so, v_t will cancel out. The time is independent of the transverse velocity - but it does depend on the axial magnetic field!

If you compare the two times, you should be able to come up with an expression that gives you a value for the charge on the electron in terms of quantities that you know or can measure: the accelerating voltage on the

85

tube, the value of the axial magnetic field, the length of the tube, and so on. (Note: determining the field in the solenoid will take some work. You will need to know the number of turns in the solenoid, its length, and the current in the coils. You will have a meter to measure the current (possibly built in to the power supply) and the number of turns on the solenoid should be noted. The necessary equation to calculate the field is in your text.)

Come up with an expression that gives the charge on the electron in terms of other quantities you know or can measure.

Once you have such an expression, measure the key quantities and test it: does it give you a reasonable value for the charge on the electron?

Summing Up

We had an old B&W TV when I was a kid that took a very long time to warm up. It also took a very long time to cool down; after you turned it off, the image would shrink to a spot on the screen, and the spot would stay there for a while—certainly the better part of a minute. One of the science books I had suggested an experiment that I did with this spot: putting a magnet up to it, to see what happens. The spot was deflected in a rather mysterious way to someone who didn't know the right hand rule. I remember doing this and being quite impressed.

Later, we had a color TV that still had tubes in it, and so took a long time to warm up and was pretty flaky. My mom kept it going for years, but it was always having problems. One of the breakages it experienced was the source of an almost-mystical experience for me. I was working nights at Frisch's Big Boy, and I came home very late, after everyone else was long asleep. I would sit downstairs and watch late-night TV to unwind. The late night selections in this era were somewhat limited; the main thing on was various religious programming. On this particular night, I was watching a rather beatific minister talking about something whose content I can't recall. I just remember that he sort of beamed, and seemed quite happy. Anyway, I got up to turn off the TV. I pushed the knob in with a resounding click, but nothing happened; the minister on the screen just kept on beaming away. I turned the knob on and off a few times, with no effect at all.

It was late, I was tired, and I was pretty suggestible. I remember clearly thinking to myself, "I am going to pull the plug on the TV, and if the program keeps on going, I am going to sit right down and pay very close attention to what this guy is saying." But when I pulled the plug, the TV went silent and dark. The on-off knob had broken, one of the last breakages before my mother pulled the plug for the final time. But I still recall this episode fondly, as one of those late-night almost-a-dream events where my first thought was not the mundane but the esoteric.

I hope your experiences with cathode ray tubes have been as mystical and entertaining.

Go in peace.

Figure 4: Side and front views of the motion of the electron for the final puzzle problem.

Side view: the electron is accelerated through a voltage V, and travels down the tube.

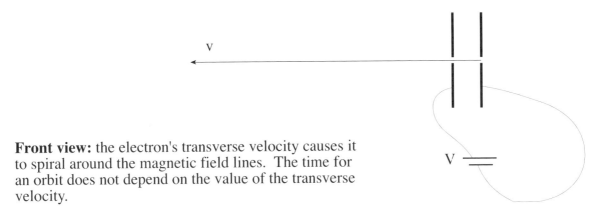

Front view: the electron's transverse velocity causes it to spiral around the magnetic field lines. The time for an orbit does not depend on the value of the transverse velocity.

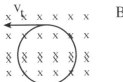

Electron Beams

Their Physics and Their Uses

Opening Remarks

"While theoretically and technically television may be feasible, commercially and financially I consider it an impossibility, a development of which we need waste little time dreaming."

- Lee DeForest, American radio pioneer, 1926

"I think there is a world market for about five computers."

- Thomas J. Watson, IBM Chairman of the Board, 1943

Despite the pessimistic pronouncements of such worthy persons as quoted above, television and the computer have become ubiquitous parts of our daily lives. It is a fact that we spend enormous amounts of time looking at images that are drawn by electron beams - or cathode rays, as they were originally named.

An experiment: get a reasonably strong magnet, and a black and white TV that you don't care about. Put the magnet up against the screen. What happens to the image? The image is created by an electron beam that is swept back and forth across the phosphor screen; the magnetic field from the magnet can deflect the beam and distort the image. UNDER NO CIRCUMSTANCES SHOULD YOU TRY THIS WITH A COLOR TELEVISION SET OR A COMPUTER MONITOR. You can permanently distort the colors on a color TV, leaving a patch where the magnet was. You can also mess up computer monitors. This has happened to some of the computers in our labs; please do not distort them further. In this and in future experiments, keep any magnets well away from the computers.

Another experiment to try, with no possible side effects: stand 3 - 4 meters back from a computer screen, and stare at it while eating something crunchy like corn chips or a granola bar. (You could also merely clack your teeth together.) What happens to the image? The vibrations from the crunching are transmitted to your eye sockets, making the image move on your retina. The image is flickering - it is redrawn more than 60 times per second on the screen by an electron beam. If the image stays still, your persistence of vision does not allow you to see this. But if the image moves around, you can see it. Wave a finger or two up and down in front of the screen; do you see the strobe effect? A tuning fork held in front of the screen can produce an even more vivid illusion.

In this lab we will study electron tubes in which the beam is easily visible. We will look at the deflection of the beam by magnetic fields, and use this to measure a basic physical property of the electron. You should think about the uses of the physics—from TV to computers—as you are working with it.

Figure 1: Warren sat for several hours trying to move his eyes fast enough to watch the electron beam sweep across the computer screen, but finally admitted defeat.

Necessary Theory

It is very important that you complete this derivation. You should start it before coming to lab, or you will not have time to finish the work that you need to do in lab.

DERIVATION

Complete the steps in the derivation outlined below.

Note: in what follows, we observe these conventions:

> V = voltage
> v = velocity

Don't mix the two up!

To make a beam of electrons, we take electrons that are emitted from a hot wire and accelerate them through a voltage to increase their speed. Suppose we accelerate an electron (with charge e) through a voltage V. The electron gains an energy:

$$E =$$

If the electron was initially moving very slowly, this energy will be equal to its kinetic energy, so we write:

$$\tfrac{1}{2}mv^2 =$$

$$v =$$

Now, suppose the electron enters a region of uniform magnetic field perpendicular to its path. It will follow a curving trajectory; this situation is illustrated in Figure 2. The magnetic field does not change the energy of the electron, but will accelerate it perpendicular to its path, causing it to follow a circular orbit until it strikes an obstruction as shown. Generally, charged particles will orbit around magnetic field lines. The radius of the circular path can be calculated; the force due to the magnetic field is given by:

$$F_{mag} =$$

There is no angle factor as the electron is always moving perpendicular to the field. This force can be equated to the centripetal force:

89

$$F_{centrip} =$$

Equating the two expressions for the force, we can find a relationship that gives the ratio of the charge of the electron to its mass in terms of V, B and r. You should work through the details to fill in the right side of this equation:

$$\frac{e}{m} =$$

Given the value of the accelerating voltage, the bending field, and the radius of the path, we can calculate the ratio of the charge to the mass of the electron, a basic physical constant.

The magnetic field in the apparatus we will be using is provided by a pair of matched Helmholtz coils. If the coils have N turns each, carry a current I and have a radius R, the field at the center of the two is given by:

$$B = \frac{8\mu_0 NI}{\sqrt{125}R}$$

This is the magnetic field that we will use in calculations.

Summing up the notation we used above:

R = radius of Helmholtz coils (m)
μ_0 = permeability of free space (N/A^2)
N = number of turns in each coil (119)
V = accelerating voltage (volts)
I = current through coils (amps)
r = radius of path of electron (m)

Plasma Frequency

We have stated that charged particles will orbit around magnetic field lines; the radius of such a circular orbit is dealt with above. Now consider the frequency of the orbit. Given the relationships used above, we can show that the angular frequency is given by:

$$\omega = \frac{v}{r} = \frac{qB}{m}$$

Notice that the second expression does not depend on the energy of the charged particle. Slower particles will move in smaller circles at the same frequency that faster particles will move in larger circles. Thus, a region of space where there are free charged particles (like the earth's ionosphere) will have certain resonant plasma or cyclotron frequencies. (This has to do with why you can bounce short wave radio off the atmosphere.) For electrons, given their small mass, the plasma frequency is pretty large even for modest field values.

Experiments and Calculations

Necessary Equipment

The apparatus for this experiment consists of the following:

Helmholtz coils and tube assembly
Power supply
Bar Magnet
Half meter stick

The coil and tube unit and the power supply contain everything needed for the experiment. The equipment needs some explaining; what follows is a description of each part of the apparatus.

The Helmholtz coil and tube base is as pictured in the left of Figure 3. The Helmholtz coils are used to provide a uniform magnetic field. In the center of the coils sits an electron tube that will provide a beam of electrons to be bent by the field. The base holds the tube and the coils in place and provides a means for making electrical connection to the different parts of the tube and the coils. The operation of the tube is as follows: a current-carrying filament heats the cathode. This causes electrons to be emitted by what is known as *thermionic emission*. A large positive voltage is applied to the plate relative to the cathode; this accelerates the electrons toward the plate. Along the way they pass the grid, which is held at a voltage intermediate between that of the cathode and the plate; this serves to focus the beam.

Figure 2: An electron is accelerated through a voltage V. It then enters a region of uniform magnetic field B. It will follow a circular path as shown. This is the basic setup that you will explore in the experiment; you will use a beam of electrons from a hot cathode that is accelerated though a voltage you apply. The resulting beam of electrons will be bent by a magnetic field from a pair of Helmholtz coils. Knowing the field, the radius of the path, and the accelerating voltage will allow you to calculate, among other things, the ratio of the charge to mass of the electron.

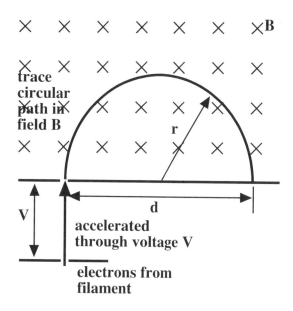

Figure 3: The electron tube that we will use appears as in the "exploded" view at the right. This tube sits in a base unit as at right; this unit allows for electrical connections to the filament, the grid and the cathode; it also holds the tube at the center of the Helmholtz coils, in the region of uniform magnetic field.

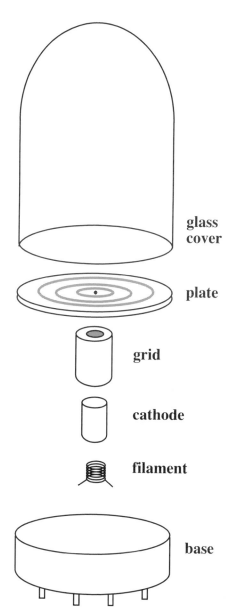

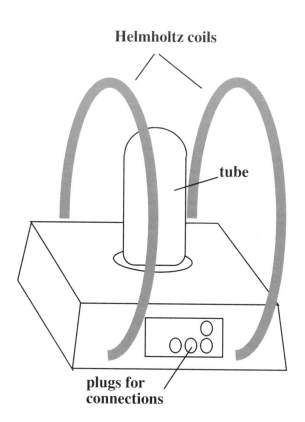

The accelerated electrons pass through a hole in the plate and into the space in the tube above the plate. The tube is filled with gas that glows when excited by the electrons, so you will be able to see the beam. It will also make a glowing spot where it hits the glass, and it will make a very bright spot where it strikes the phosphor rings on the plate. Basically, you will be able to keep track of the beam pretty well.

If a current is passed through the Helmholtz coils, a magnetic field is produced that will bend the beam in a circular arc. You will be able to see this bending. The beam can be bent over so that it strikes the plate. There are four circles inscribed on the plate, of radii 2.0, 1.5, 1.0 and 0.5 cm. The inscribed grooves are filled with a phosphorescent compound like that on the screen of an oscilloscope. When the beam hits one of the circles, it will make a glowing dot where it hits. Thus you will be able to precisely determine the radius of the path of the beam.

The voltages to the grid and plate and the currents for the filament and the Helmholtz coils are provided by the power supply unit. All of the connections have already been made; all you must do is turn on the supply and make adjustments. A view of the face of the power supply unit is given in Figure 4. It is important that you know what each dial and plug is for; here is a description of the different parts.

On-off switch: **Turn the device off while you are not making measurements!** The filament has a finite lifetime, and there is no need to keep it hot while measurements are not being made. After you first turn the supply on, it will take a minute or so before the cathode heats up. Be patient.

Filament: These plugs are for providing the current to the filament in the electron tube. They have already been set at the proper voltage; do not make any adjustments.

Plate voltage: The plugs from this supply are connected to the top plate that you see in the electron tube. Applying a positive voltage will accelerate the free electrons in the tube to form a beam. You can adjust the speed of the beam by adjusting the value of this voltage. Note the following:

1) The meter at top records the voltage of this supply only when the switch above the dials is to the left. Keep the switch in this position!

2) The voltage can be turned up to 500 V, but anything more than 150 V can damage the tube. For this reason, do not turn the voltage up to more than 140 V.

3) For voltages that are too small, the beam is ill-defined. Do not use plate voltages of less than 60 V.

Grid voltage: You will adjust this control to get a nice, sharp beam. There is no need to measure this voltage; just set it to get the best beam. You will have to readjust this voltage whenever you change the plate voltage.

Helmholtz coil supply: This supply provides a current to the Helmholtz coils which will deflect the beam; the meter measures the current provided. If you switch the plugs on the supply, you switch the direction of the current through the coils. Please turn the current to zero before you make any changes!

Measurements and Calculations

The lab will be darkened for this experiment. The lights should be set so that you can see the beam (which is quite dim!) but so that you can still read the dials on your instruments.

The connections between the different parts of the power supply and the electron tube should already be in place; please leave them as they are! If you feel that they have been altered, please ask your instructor for assistance. Check out the different parts of the apparatus and assure yourself that you know what everything does.

Measure the radius of the Helmholtz coils; you will need this number later.

Obtain a Good Beam

Turn all dials all the way down, and turn on the power supply. After some seconds, you should see

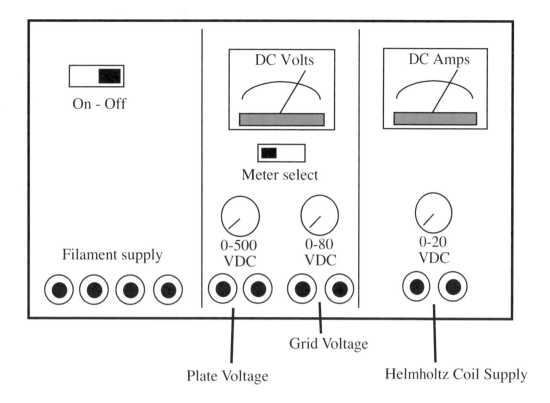

Figure 4: This is the face of the power supply unit you will be using. The connections will be made; you will need only to adjust the dials. The operation of the different controls is discussed in the text.

an orange glow in the electron tube; this is due to the heating up of the filament. Let it warm up for a minute or so.

Turn the plate voltage to 100 V. (Watch the dial carefully.) You should see a blue spray of electrons coming out of the hole in the plate. (Well, you don't see the electrons, but the light from atoms they strike and excite.) Dial up the grid voltage carefully until you obtain a nice, sharp beam. This takes some care, as a small change in voltage makes a big change in the beam shape.

Now Deflect the Sucker

Now that you have a nice beam, it is time to deflect it. Take the bar magnet you have been given, and note the sense of the field. Place the magnet so that the beam is moving perpendicular to this field, and note the deflection of the beam. Now try this with the other pole of the magnet; what do

you observe? Feel free to do other experiments; as the field from the magnet diverges, you can get a "magnetic bottle" effect. Ask your instructor for details.

Next, bend the beam with the coils. Dial up the voltage to the coils, and watch the beam bend. If you are careful, you can bend the beam so that it goes between the plate and the glass and almost forms a complete circle. Change the direction of the current; what happens to the beam? (Note: turn the current to zero before doing this!)

The beam is bent in a semicircular arc; if the current is large enough, the beam should hit the plate. Adjust the current until the beam hits the outermost of the rings on the plate; you should see a glowing spot on the ring where the beam hits. This is how you want to take data: if you adjust the beam like so, the diameter of the circle of the beam's travel is just equal to the radius of the circle on the plate. Four circles are marked, at radius .5, 1.0, 1.5 and

2.0 cm. Set the beam so that it just hits one of these circles.

PREDICTION

If you make a slight increase in the plate voltage, what should happen to the radius of the path of the beam? Predict this, and test.

PREDICTION

If you make a small decrease in the plate voltage, what should happen to the radius of the path of the beam? Again, predict and then test.

PUZZLE

In both cases, the size of the circular path changes; given the above information concerning the plasma frequency, what can you say about the *time* for the electrons to traverse the semicircle for the different voltages? If instead of changing the accelerating voltage you change the bending field, what does this do to the time?

Taking data

Set the beam to hit one of the circles, and note the following:

- radius of the circle hit by beam
- plate voltage
- Helmholtz current

Note: due to imperfections in the manufacture of the tube, you will most likely find that there is an asymmetry: the same field will bend the beam more in one direction than the other. To correct for this systematic error, you should take data in first one direction then the other, and then average. Reverse the current and measure the current necessary to hit the circle bending the beam the other way, and record the data. You should use this average value in your calculations.

Given the data you have taken, you will be able to calculate a value for e/m for the electron using the equations given above. There is a complication, though: the radius of the electron orbit must be obtained from the radius of the plate circle. It is not just half; there is a correction due to the fact that the beam begins bending below the surface of the plate, so you do not get a full semicircle. You correct for this according to the following formula, where r_{plate} is the radius of the circle on the plate:

$$r = [(r_{plate}/2)^2 + (.254 cm)^2]^{1/2}$$

Calculate e/m for the data point you have taken. How does your value agree with the accepted value? If you have time, do the same measurement and calculation for other values of the radius. If you get three values, for 2.0, 1.5, and 1.0 cm (.5 cm doesn't work very well), you can look at the three values to get some idea of the uncertainty in your determination. Does the value for e/m you get agree with the accepted value to within error? If not, what mistakes could you have made? (Note: if you are off by a factor of 10, 100 or 1000, you probably have a problem with units. If you are off by a factor of 2 or 4, you probably forgot to divide or multiply somewhere. Do you want a radius or a diameter? Which number did you use?)

Calculations

There are a few interesting calculations that you can make for your beam:

PUZZLE

Calculate the velocity of the electrons in your beam. You will find that they are moving pretty fast. Are they moving fast enough that relativity is an issue? How would you know?

PUZZLE

Calculate the plasma frequency of your beam. Convert the angular frequency to a real frequency. What do you get? What does this correspond to on the electromagnetic scale? AM radio? FM radio? Microwaves?

Summary

The opening remarks to this experiment discussed the many uses of electron beams in our modern society, especially in computer monitors and television. You may have heard a computer monitor called a CRT, or cathode ray tube. This term for the electron beam, a cathode ray, persists from the days before the nature of these rays were known. In an experiment similar to the one that you have performed, J.J. Thompson showed that these rays, which came from the heated cathode in a vacuum tube, were in fact composed of discrete particles; he also measured their charge-to-mass ratio. He argued that these particles, which he called "corpuscles" and which later came to be known as "electrons," were constituents of all atoms. This was the beginning of our modern understanding of atomic structure. So the experiment that you have just performed has a rich history indeed.

Early investigations using cathode rays were important for other reasons. When highly accelerated beams of electrons strike a target in an evacuated tube, they produce x-rays; this is how this particular form of electromagnetic radiation was discovered.

Does this mean, I hear you thinking, that when the electron beam in my television strikes the screen, it gives off x-rays? You bet. So if you sit close to the screen, are you being irradiated? No. This was a concern of some old sets, but newer TVs must meet rigorous standards of emission; they are carefully shielded so that the x-rays that are emitted are attenuated.

Bending electron beams to make images is a remarkable technology; but has it made the world a better place? Maybe, maybe not. I quote from a 1927 lecture to the British Association for the Advancement of Science by E.A. Burroughs:

"After all, we could get on very happily if aviation, [radio], television and the like advanced no further than at present. Dare I even suggest... that the sum total of human happiness would not necessarily be reduced if for ten years every physical and chemical laboratory were closed and the patient and resourceful energy displayed in them transferred to the lost art of getting on together and finding the formula for making both ends meet in the scale of human life. Much, of course, we should lose by this universal scientific holiday... but human happiness would not necessarily suffer."

Go in peace.

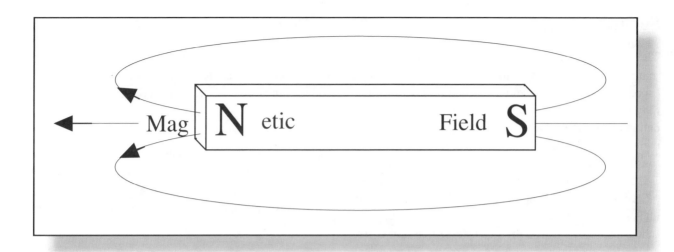

Opening Remarks

In today's lab you will be studying magnets and magnetic fields. Their mysterious properties, their invisible forces were the basis of much interest in past centuries—as well as today.

"This kind of stone [the magnet] restores husbands to wives and increases charm and elegance in speech. Moreover, along with honey, it cures dropsy, spleen, fox mange, and burns. When placed on the head of a chaste woman, [the magnet] causes its poison to surround her immediately, but if she is an adulteress she will instantly remove herself from bed for fear of an apparition. There are mountains made of such stones, and they attract and dissolve ships of iron."

- Bartholomew the Englishman, encyclopedist, 13th century AD

There are still people who claim to have beneficial medical applications from magnets. This is one of those areas where there is no good clinical data to back up the claims - just lots of anecdotal evidence. There may well be something going on, but I rather suspect that much of the benefit comes from the fact that magnets are just so neat that folks figure they have to help make them well.

In this lab we will be concerned with a more prosaic side of magnetism: the fields from current sources and permanent magnets.

Necessary Theory

The Hall Probe

One device that you will use in today's lab to measure magnetic fields is known as a Hall probe. It depends on what is known as the Hall effect to produce a voltage that is proportional to a magnetic field, thus allowing a measurement of the field. The physics behind the operation of this probe is illustrated in Figure 2. There are two things to note in particular:

• Only the component of the field perpendicular to the Hall sample is measured.

• Reversing the sense of the field will reverse the sense of the voltage measured.

The Hall probe can thus give a measurement of the direction of the field in addition to its strength: the probe is rotated until the voltage reading is maximized; at this point, the probe sample will be perpendicular to the field. The sense of the voltage will tell you which way the field goes. Nifty, eh? The probe you will use in the lab has a Hall wafer with a white protective top; keep the plane of the wafer perpendicular to any fields that you wish to measure.

Permanent Magnets

We will have a variety of permanent magnets for you to explore. You should first measure the field of a bar magnet. The magnet has a north pole and

96

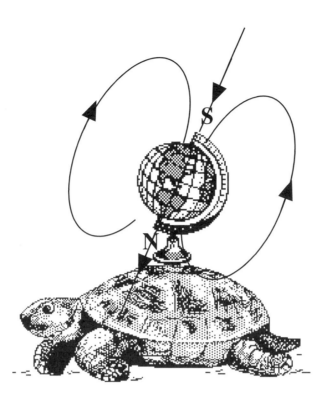

Figure 1: A view of the globe of the earth. Note the magnetic field lines. It turns out that the north pole of the earth is a magnetic south pole; the south pole is the earth's magnetic north pole. Think about it: the north pole of a magnet is attracted to the earth's north pole, which thus must be a magnetic south pole. Also muddying the waters is the fact that the earth's magnetic poles are offset from the rotational poles; the north magnetic pole (which, of course, is a magnetic south pole) is located on Canada's Baffin Island, quite far from the rotational pole. Which direction would a compass point here? Down, if it could.

In this diagram, the earth is shown according to the primitive cosmological view which held that the earth rode on the back of a turtle. Of course we now know that this is not true; the current view is that the earth rides on the back of a turtle who rides on the back of an elephant who rides on the back of a '56 Chevy Bel-Air.

a south pole; it produces a dipole field. You will have devices to measure the field direction and strength, to sketch out the basic pattern of field lines produced by this basic element.

In addition, there will be a variety of different ceramic magnets available. These will be of a variety of shapes and sizes; an important property that you can measure for these magnets is the direction of the magnetization. Where is the axis along which you find the north and south poles? This will not always be the long axis of the magnet! You should also note that a magnet can have more than two poles.

A caveat: please do not use the magnets to distort the display of the computers. This can cause irreparable damage.

The Solenoid

A solenoid is a long coil of wire. For the mathematics that you have learned to apply, the length of the solenoid must be much greater than the diameter. In addition, the distance between successive turns must be small compared to the diameter.

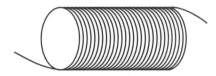

Solenoids are usually drawn as having a circular cross section, as above; this is not a necessary condition. The solenoid that you will use in the lab will have a square cross section.

The magnetic field of a solenoid has the following properties:

• The field inside the solenoid is uniform, and is parallel to the axis of the solenoid.

• The field strength depends only on the spacing of the turns and the current in the wire.

• The field is small outside the solenoid.

• The field drops off rapidly at the ends of the solenoid.

You should review the descriptions of the field of a solenoid that you have seen in class.

The Circular Current Loop, or Coil

In this lab you will also be able to look at the field of a flat coil. Of interest in this case are:

• The variation of field strength close to the coil (small variation).

• The variation of the field far away from the coil ($1/x^3$).

• The direction of the field in and around the coil.

The coil will produce a basic dipole field. Far away from the coil, the field should look like that of a bar magnet.

The Field of the Earth

What is the direction of the earth's field at Fort Collins? There are two components: a component parallel to the earth that points roughly south, and a component that points perpendicular to the surface of the earth. A compass free to move up and down will point down, so the angle of the field, taking into account this component, is known as the dip angle.

The makers of the field sensor we have claim that on the 200x setting it can measure the direction of the earth's field. Try it and see! Rotate the probe until the maximum value is obtained. What is the dip angle, roughly; you might be surprised by how large it is. (Note: in making this measurement, you must be careful to be well away from other fields. This might not be possible in our magnet-rich lab.)

And now, on to:

Measurements and Calculations

Equipment Needed

You will receive the following pieces of equipment for making fields:

> Solenoid and Coil
> Power supply for solenoid and coil
> Bar Magnet

and some other permanent magnets. You will also receive equipment for measuring fields:

> Magnaprobe
> Hall probe used with computer, interface,
>   Data Logger

The power supply can put out a lot of current; please be careful that you keep the current values less than 4 amps so that the coil and solenoid don't heat up. In addition, please turn the supply off when you are not using it. The power supplies will smell a bit when they get hot; this is normal, but it can be annoying, so keep them off when you aren't using them.

Figure 2: A semiconductor sample has electrons flowing through it as noted. A field B that is perpendicular to the sample as shown causes a force F on the electrons as noted. This pushes the electrons to the right; they will tend to pile up on this side, until a voltage develops that offsets the force of the magnetic field. This voltage can be measured; it is proportional to the strength of the field. The sign of the voltage will depend on the sense of the field; if the field direction is reversed, so will be the sign of the voltage. Note also that only the perpendicular component of the field will be measured.

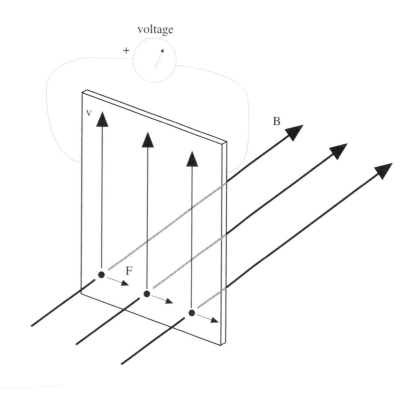

Figure 3: The Hall probe, as noted, puts out a voltage that is positive or negative depending on the sense of the magnetic field. The magnitude of the voltage is proportional to the magnitude of the magnetic field, but is very, very small. In order for the interface to measure this small voltage, it is necessary for the voltage to be amplified. The box that the probe connects to has a two-position switch that can be set for 10x amplification (for strong magnets) or 200x amplification (for weaker fields). The program that you will use to measure the output of the probe is calibrated for these two settings. When you start the program, you will get a window as at right. The window will display the results of measurements that you make, with units in gauss. In order to have the appropriate calibration, you will need to choose a scale for the 10x probe or the 200x probe setting. You can do this by clicking on the title for the vertical axis; you will get a pop-up menu.

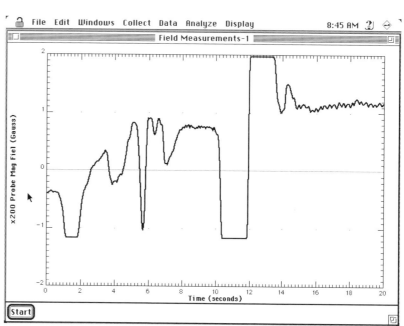

The magnaprobe is a small bar magnet mounted so that it can swivel in all directions. When held in a region of reasonably strong magnetic field, the little magnet swings to align itself with the field. This allows you to determine the direction of the field. One caution: you don't want to touch the probe to stronger magnets, as this could alter the magnetization.

The operation of the Hall probe is discussed above. The magnaprobe is quicker for determining the direction of the field at any point, but the Hall probe will give an output that gives a quantitative measure of the field at any point. The computer uses the program Data Logger to collect and display values of the voltage. Details are presented in Figure 3. Note that either device will give you a direction for the field; since magnetic field is a vector, please be sure to note the direction of fields that you measure.

You will also have a few items that you (possibly) used in an earlier lab:

> Genecon
> Long-ish wire
> Compass
> Magnet swing device

These are some items that you will use for some warm-up exercises having to do with currents and magnetic fields.

Fields of A Bar Magnet

Set your bar magnet on the table, with a piece of paper under it. Use your Magnaprobe to sketch out the direction of the field around the magnet. Sketch out several field lines, as you did earlier in the semester with electric fields. Where are the north and south poles? Are they at the ends of the magnet?

PREDICTION

Before you measure the strength of the field, predict: where is the field strongest? Where is the field weakest? How can you tell this from the field lines that you have drawn?

Make a prediction, and test. Note: use the 10x setting on the probe. You can use your field lines as a guide as to how to orient the probe. Does this work as you expect?

Next, use your field probe to measure the strength of the field at different points around the magnet. Is the field strongest where you predicted it would be?

Other Permanent Magnets

There will be some other magnets for you to experiment with. These will come in a kit; please keep them in their holder when not in use, and do not allow the magnets to stick to each other!

For two or three other magnets, notice:

• Are there two poles, or more?

• What is the axis of the magnetization?

You will probably find that there aren't that many "bar" magnets around—ones with the north pole on one end and the south pole on the other. In order to have strong fields near the magnet (and not so strong farther away) other configurations are the rule.

Fields and Currents #1

You are going to do some exercises having to do with currents and the magnetic fields they produce. Here is an exercise that you may have done earlier in the semester, presented as a warmup. Take a Genecon, and use a hookup wire to connect the two leads. Now take the wire and wrap it repeatedly around your compass, with the wire parallel to the needle, like so:

Hold the compass level, so that it can swivel. Normally, the compass lines up with the magnetic field of the earth. Now turn the crank on your Genecon. What happens now?

PUZZLE

The compass lines itself up with a magnetic field. What is the sense of the magnetic field from the coil of wire?

If you have talked about the right hand rule,

can you use the right hand rule to determine the direction of current flow necessary to produce this field? Does this agree with the direction of current flow you would determine by looking at the Genecon?

Fields, Currents and Forces

We won't do anything with it in this lab, but it is worthwhile noting that magnetic fields make forces on moving charges - currents. Take a Genecon and connect it up to the so-called magnet swing device. The swing is a wire which is connected to two hooks; the wire is free to swing, while staying connected to the hooks.

Be sure that the wire is free to swing and is making good contact, and crank your Genecon. What happens? Now turn the crank the other way. What happens now? Turn the crank back and forth; if

you are careful to match your cranking speed to the speed of the swing, you can get a good amplitude going!

PUZZLE

If you have talked about the right hand rule, can you use the right hand rule to determine the direction that current is flowing in the wire, given the force on the wire? Does this agree with the direction of current flow you would determine by looking at the Genecon?

Field of Solenoid

In the theory section, certain properties of the solenoid field were mentioned. The most interesting fact about a solenoid is that the field is almost entirely confined to the region inside the coils. The solenoid that you will use has been skillfully designed so that the field probe that you will use can fit in between the coils, allowing you to measure the field inside. Use the field probe to probe the

field of the solenoid:

• Bringing the probe in from the side, how much does the field change when the probe is moved from just outside to just inside? Is the field in fact largely contained in the solenoid?

• Is the field reasonably uniform inside the solenoid?

PUZZLE

Measure the field at the center (of the long axis) of the solenoid. Now, predict what the field should be at the ends. (You don't need a calibrated probe for this, and you don't have one. Just note what fraction the field should be: 1/3? 1/4?) Once you have made a prediction, test it. Is the result what you expected? If not, can you explain why?

Field of Coil

The field of the coil should be similar to that of the bar magnet. Use the Magnaprobe to note the field directions around the coil; is the variation as you expect?

PUZZLE

Where should the field of the coil be strongest? Make a prediction, then test. Note: to get a valid test, you will need to be certain that the probe is aligned with the field to be measured!

Look at the variation of the field along the axis; it should fall off slowly at first, then rapidly as you move farther away. Can you explain why this is—qualitatively, or in terms of an equation?

Field of the Earth

As noted above, the makers of the field probe claim that the probe on the 200x setting is sensitive enough to measure the field of the earth. The main thing you can do is to rotate the probe around until the maximum reading is found; this will give you the direction of the earth's field. As noted, this may not work, as there are lots of magnets around in the lab to muddy the waters. It might be worth a try, though. Of interest: what is the *direction* of the field?

Helmholtz Coils

If a very uniform field is needed over a reasonably small area, a pair of field coils (known as Helmholtz coils) may suffice. The coils are aligned coaxially, and the field along the axis near the center is quite uniform—for the correct coil spacing!

PUZZLE

Can you find the optimal spacing for a Helmholtz pair? Find another group to work with (or borrow from an empty table). Find the best spacing to give a uniform field. You can check this empirical result with the theoretical value, which your instructor will have, or that may be in your text. Can you explain (theoretically) why the field is so uniform at this particular separation?

Other Fields...

Recently there has been a lot of interest in low frequency AC fields. There is some evidence that such fields may increase the chance of certain types of cancer. The evidence so far is not that strong; the effect is certainly not a large one, but the matter obviously deserves further inquiry. Anything that has AC current in it gives off AC magnetic fields; the amount and a person's exposure depends on the device and its use. A blender, for instance, uses quite a bit of current and may develop a large AC field while it is in use, but people don't stand next to running blenders all that often. An electric blanket, on the other hand, has only a small current going through it, and so produces a small field, but it is designed to lie on top of a person all night, thus giving long-term, full-body exposure.

Your Hall probe can be used to measure these AC fields. You should change the data rate to a high enough rate to give a reliable picture of a 60 Hz wave. (Don't use the maximum setting; this will needlessly slow things down. 1000 points a second is fine.) You must also change the length of time for which you take data, so that you don't use up all of the computer's memory.

Various devices will be around whose fields you can measure: how about your computer? (Note: there are different places of note: on the front of the monitor, on the case, etc. Try to find a field near a fan or a power supply; this is often a likely place. How about your lab power supply (when it is on, and supplying current to something)? Measure the fields around these different objects, and other devices around the lab, and see what you find. How large are the fields (in amplitude) compared with, say, the earth's field?

Summing Up

Magnets and magnetic fields have been of great interest since antiquity. There is something that still seems magical to me about how a magnet will attract and stick to a piece of steel, and how the needle in a compass will rotate itself to align with the field of the earth.

Something else to note: magnetism is, really, the same force as in electrostatics: the Coulomb's Law force plus relativity gives magnetism. This is an example of unification: the idea that what appear on the surface to be different phenomena are, at the root, the same thing. This is a remarkable idea that has driven much of the most exciting work in physics over the past half-century or so.

Go in peace.

Figure 4: It often seems that almost everything around us is touted to cause one form of malady or another. It is necessary to keep all of this in perspective. And to concentrate on the positive: naps, for instance, are most certainly good for you. So even if you fall asleep in your Physics class, you are at least doing a healthful thing. Don't try it in lab, though.

Faraday's Law and

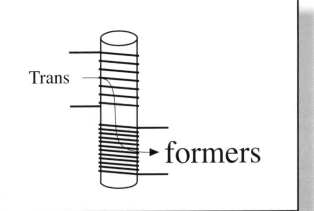

Trans formers

Opening Remarks

As we began the section on Coulomb's Law with a quote from Coulomb, we can do no less for Faraday.

"One day, Sir, you may tax it."

- Michael Faraday, speaking to Gladstone, British Chancellor of the Exchequer, who had asked about the practical uses of electricity.

Michael Faraday, the largely self-educated son of a blacksmith, eventually came to be regarded as the greatest experimental scientist of the 1800's. His contributions to the study of electricity and magnetism were far-ranging and productive. He was also a brilliant public lecturer, and was able to think on his feet—as revealed by the above quote.

In this lab we will explore the basic phenomenon that bears his name: the fact that a changing magnetic field can induce an electric field, and thus a voltage. This principle is central to the production and use of electricity, for instance in the generator, by which virtually all of our electricity is produced. The principle is also behind the operation of the transformer, as we will see in the lab.

Necessary Theory

Principle of Induction

In Figure 2, a bar magnet is shown moving toward a loop of wire. As you know by now, this causes a change of flux through the loop, and thus an emf will be generated around it. If the magnet ceases to move, the emf will also cease. Then, if the magnet is taken away, an emf will be generated in the opposite sense, according to the dictates of Lenz's law. (Note: one of the descendants of this Lenz teaches at CSU, though not in Physics.) It is worthwhile spending some time testing out this principle, using magnets and coils; this is just what you will have a chance to do in this lab.

The changes in voltage that occur are rapid, and can be positive or negative. The changes may also be quite small. We will use a galvanometer to sense the small signals; they can record small positive or negative changes in current (and thus emf). You won't get any record of the changes, so you will have to be a quick observer!

Ferromagnetism

The magnetic field produced by a coil of wire with a current through it is generally quite small. In order to increase the strength of the field, we can use a ferromagnetic material. Ferromagnetic materials have regions of strong local magnetic fields (domains) that are generally randomly oriented; see the first illustration in Figure 3. Now suppose we apply a small field to the material; this has the effect of "lining up" the domains. What actually happens is that domains that are oriented in the same sense as the applied field will grow at the expense of domains that are not favorably oriented. The net result is that the material will now be strongly magnetized: it will produce a field in the same sense

104

Figure 1: Years ago, when I began writing the lab manuals, it became my habit to insert a Figure 1 graphic that was purely silly; there was no real point to it. It did keep me writing, I suppose; writing a lab manual is not as action-packed and glamorous as you might imagine. But, over the years, I change these, or tone them down. I won't even start to explain what the caption for this one was.

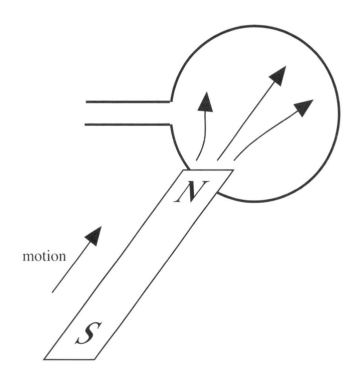

Figure 2: A magnet is moved toward a loop of wire. As discussed, this produces an emf in the loop. This is a phenomenon on which you will have a chance to make exhaustive investigations.

as the applied field that may be 1000x as strong as the applied field. The total field is thus quite large; the ferromagnetic material has, we might say, amplified the small applied field.

There are two basic kinds of ferromagnetic materials: "soft" and "hard." The hard materials are used in permanent magnets; they are hard to magnetize, but once magnetized, they will maintain their magnetization. Soft materials are easy to magnetize, but when the external field is removed, they lose most of their magnetization. These materials are used in transformer cores; we want the materials to respond quickly to changes in the applied field. The transformer system you will use in the lab comes with a core of laminated iron that will work in this fashion. It will retain a small amount of magnetization, but generally it will only be magnetized in proportion to a small applied field.

Solenoid

A solenoid, or a coil of wire, has the strongest field in its center. If a piece of ferromagnetic material is placed near a solenoid and a current is passed through the solenoid, a field is produced. The ferromagnetic material is magnetized in the same sense as the solenoid field. If you consider the fields of the solenoid and the material, you can see that the material will feel a force toward the region of greatest field strength: i.e., the center of the solenoid. This means that the material will be pulled into the solenoid.

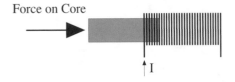
Force on Core

I

Solenoids with iron cores are used in this fashion on automatic door locks on cars, "buzzers" that people use to let others into an apartment building (the buzzing is because an AC current is used), and many other places that you have seen. Once you start looking for them, they turn up everywhere.

You will get a chance to explore this principle in the lab.

Transformers

Consider Figure 4. A current is passed through a coil of wire; this produces a magnetic field. A second coil is placed near the first; some of the field from the first will go through the second, but only a very small amount.

Now, the coils are placed on a U-shaped piece of ferromagnetic material. This will dramatically increase the field strength and concentrate the flux so that the flux through one coil is largely shared by the second. This sharing of flux can be increased by adding another piece to close the U; this extra piece will be magnetized also, and will direct the field so that the flux through the two coils is nearly the same: flux produced in one coil will go though the other.

Now recall what you have learned about changing flux. The sharing of flux means that a changing current in one coil will induce a changing voltage in the other, and vice-versa. The important part of this is that an AC voltage on one coil, the primary, induces a signal on the other, the secondary, whose voltage is related to that on the primary by the ratio of turns on the primary and the secondary:

$$V_s = \frac{N_s}{N_p} V_p$$

Now, since the transformer (ideally) puts out as much power from the secondary as it draws at the primary, we can also say:

$$I_p V_p = I_s V_s$$

Of course, our transformers are far from ideal! You will see this when you use them. You will almost certainly see less voltage at the secondary than you predict.

The details of the above are worked out in your text; you should review the derivation. This principle, that of the transformer, is of great importance in the practical uses of electricity. By using a transformer, one may increase or decrease the voltage of a signal, with very little loss of power. This means that AC voltage can be easily changed from one voltage to another, and thus optimized for the intended use. For instance, electrical power is generated at

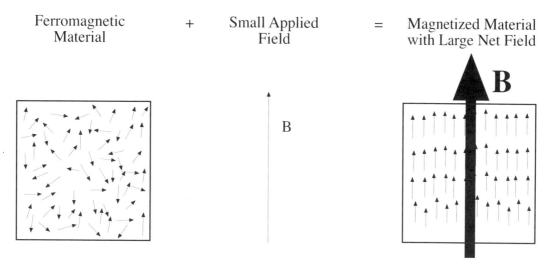

Figure 3: A sample of ferromagnetic material contains regions that are strongly magnetized, but the field directions are randomly oriented. A small applied field can organize the domains by increasing the size of domains with fields that are parallel to the applied field at the expense of the other domains. This produces a sample that is strongly magnetized, with a net field in the direction of the applied field, but much stronger. (Note: the alignment of the domains is exaggerated in this diagram.)

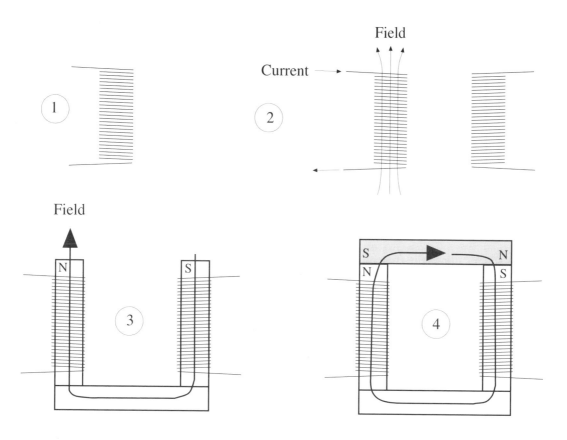

Figure 4: In 1), we see a coil. In 2), a current in the coil creates a field; some of the field will pass through a second coil, but only a small fraction. Adding a ferromagnetic core in 3) increases the field, and insures that much of the field is shared between the two coils. This is enhanced by making the core a closed loop in 4); with the geometry of the core like this, most of the field will be shared between the two cores. This sets up a transformer, in which a changing current in one core will produce a changing

tens of thousands of volts, transmitted over long distance at hundreds of thousands of volts (thus minimizing power losses during transmission), then stepped down to hundreds of volts for local distribution. Eventually, the voltage is reduced to 115 V rms for household use. But when you plug in a device such as a radio, this voltage is stepped down to some tens of volts and changed to DC before it is used. So the electrical energy we use has been changed from one voltage to another several times between generation and use. The efficiency possible in transmitting AC power (at high voltage) was the decisive factor in favor of using this form of electricity for the national grid. Thomas Edison championed the cause of DC power, but lost out in this case.

You will have a chance to explore the workings of transformers in lab. You will get a set of four coils that can be placed in pairs over a common core. The core is in two parts as in Figure 4. You will drive the primary with an AC power supply, and measure voltages on the primary and the secondary. You will measure voltages using a digital multimeter; note that this will return a single value which is the rms value. If you are not sure what this means, you should review your text.

Experiments and Calculations

Equipment

Each group will require the following equipment:

> AC power supply
> DC power supply
> Digital multimeter (DMM)
> Galvanometer
> Magnet
> Two-piece core unit
> 4 transformer coils: 1 of 200 turns,
>   2 of 400, and 1 of 800
> Lamp (to use as a load)

The transformer coils consist of 200, 400 or 800 turns of wire on a plastic spindle. These spindles will just fit over the iron core. When two coils

are placed over the core, they form a transformer, though not a perfect one. When current is passed through one coil, a magnetic field is produced in the coil. This will magnetize the core; most of the magnetic field due to the coil will be in the core. This core passes through the second coil, so the magnetic field from the first coil is mostly shared by the second. A changing current in the first coil will induce a changing magnetic field in the core, and this will in turn induce an emf in the second coil: thus is a transformer made.

The galvanometer can be used to measure small currents. A changing flux through a coil will induce an emf in it, causing current to flow. A sensitive ammeter (a galvanometer) can measure this current. The flux through the coil can be changed by using a permanent magnet, or by using another coil as a field source. Both of these techniques will be used in this lab.

Making AC voltage measurements

The purpose of the digital multimeter will be to measure voltages. In characterizing the operation of a transformer, you will want to know the voltages on the primary and on the secondary coils. You can use the DMM to make these measurements. It is important to understand the measurement that is being made. On the front table in the lab there will be a signal generator connected to an oscilloscope so that you can see the voltage output by the signal generator. In addition, there will be a DMM connected to it. The DMM measures what is known as an rms (root mean square) value. What is the relationship between the peak value of the voltage as measured on the oscilloscope and the rms value measured by the DMM? (Note: if you don't know how to read an oscilloscope, ask your instructor for assistance.) Given what you have learned about AC circuits, predict what the relationship should be. Once you have done this, compare the readings on the oscilloscope and the DMM to see if this relationship holds.

The rms value can be used as a measure of the voltage of an AC signal. It is an average voltage that is especially chosen to work well with power calculations: we know that $P = V^2/R$ for

DC circuits; for AC circuits, the average power is the same: $P = V^2/R$, as long as the voltage used is the rms voltage.

When we measure AC voltages in this lab, keep in mind that you are measuring rms values. The peak values are higher!

Magnets and coils

Connect the 800-turn coil to the galvanometer. As in Figure 2, moving a magnet with respect to the coil may produce an emf in the coil. You will be given a variety of magnets to use. Can you induce a current in your coil? Try different orientations of the magnet and coil, and make some conclusions. Some cautions:

• Please keep the magnets away from each other!

• Keep the magnets well away from the galvanometer. The magnets can affect the reading.

PUZZLE

Moving a magnet briskly in and out of a coil will make an emf that goes one direction then the other. Can you explain what is happening in terms of magnetic induction? Can you make an emf that only goes positive? One that only goes negative? How must you arrange the magnet and the coil to get the largest possible deflection? Can you explain why in terms of the magnetic field of the magnet?

Coils and coils

Now we will begin to look at the production of a transformer. Choose two of your coils, and place them over the U-shaped portion of your core. Add the cross piece to complete the loop. Choose one of the coils to be the primary; connect it to your power supply. The other is the secondary; connect it to the galvanometer. Use the DC power supply. For now, keep the power supply turned off, but turn the voltage dial up all the way.

PREDICTION

When you suddenly turn the power on, what should happen to the needle on the galvanometer? Make and record a prediction as to how the needle should move. Will it swing to one side, then swing back? Swing to one side and stay? Swing to one side, then the other side?

Once you have made a prediction, test it. Turn on the power; what do you observe? Now turn off the power. What happens to the needle now? Does it move immediately? Is the deflection the same as before? Explain. Do you notice a time delay? Think about what might cause this. (Hint: there is a big capacitor in the power supply.)

Try this with different groupings of the coils: 200 on the primary, 800 on the secondary; 800 on the primary, 200 on the secondary, etc. What differences do you note among the different combinations? It might well be that the limiting factor in this experiment is the resistance of the galvanometer, and thus no great differences are seen.

Solenoid

If your AC supply is connected to a coil from your set, and the iron core placed partially in the coil, when the supply is turned on, the coil will be pulled in. This is the principle of the solenoid.

Connect up a 200 turn coil to your power supply, and put the single iron ore piece (not the U piece) part way into the coil. Turn the power on (briefly; do not let it linger!); what happens to the core?

PREDICTION

Suppose you were to try the same thing with a 400 turn coil. Would the effect be larger or smaller—that is, would the core be pulled in more strongly, or less strongly? Think about it, and make a prediction.

After you have made a prediction, test it.

PUZZLE

Can you explain what you have just seen? Hint: think about the current in the coils. Is it the same for both? Why or why not? Think about the thickness and the length of the wires, and their resistance. How would this affect things?

Can you see how this solenoid principle could be used in practical devices? Solenoids are used in car door locks, to work valves, and in many other areas.

Transformers

Choose two of the coils and place them on the U-shaped part of the core; add the cross piece. Choose one coil to be the primary, and one to be the secondary. Connect the primary to the AC supply. Measure the rms voltage on the primary.

PREDICTION

Based on the turns ratio of the two coils and the voltage seen and the primary, predict what rms voltage you will measure on the secondary.

Measure the actual secondary voltage that you get. Is it what you expected?

If the value was smaller, note: there are some losses, but the percent loss should be the same for all combinations. Choose another combination of primary and secondary. Measure the voltage on the primary, and given the turns ratio and the loss you expect...

PREDICTION

...predict what voltage you should see on the secondary. Is this what you see? Now try another combination, and another. Do you observe the ratios you expect?

It is also instructive to look at how the core affects the transformer. With the current on and the meter hooked up to the secondary, remove the cross piece. You should feel some force keeping the cross piece connected to the U; it will actually take a bit of a tug to remove it. Once it is removed, what happens to the voltage on the secondary? How can you explain this?

If you have time, try some other turns ratios. One other possibility: can you connect these transformers one after another? You have been using the transformers without drawing any current on the secondary. When you add a load, you might see some changes. Try it and see! Just be sure to return all the equipment to its proper place.

Summing Up

In this lab you have the chance to explore the phenomenon of induction, the creation of an emf by a changing magnetic field, and some of the uses to which it is put. This is one of the more interesting parts of PH 142, and one of the most practically important. The ability to efficiently transform voltages so that electricity can be transmitted at high voltages then used at low voltages is what has made it possible for such large areas of the country to be electrified. Early systems of lighting (such as Edison's DC system) could extend no farther than 10 miles, and by the end of the line the bulbs were getting pretty dim. Now we have a national power grid with electricity going great distances to perform the humble task of lighting the bulb by which you read this manual. Perhaps a fraction of this energy was generated by a power plant on the lower reaches of the Colorado River—or even Niagara Falls.

Some history: as was noted in the opening, Michael Faraday was a brilliant scientist. He was also a moral one, refusing to participate in the production of poison gas for military uses. The moral dimension to science, that we must consider the uses of the technologies we create, was brought home forcibly at the close of WWII, with the dropping of the atomic bomb. One of the chief developers of the bomb, J. Robert Oppenheimer, later became a leading proponent for strong limits on its deployment. (His brother taught at CU, and developed the introductory physics lab there—which is still in use.) In a lecture at MIT in 1947, he summed up his loss of innocence at the first use of atomic weapons:

"In some sort of crude sense which no vulgarity, no humor, no overstatement can quite extinguish, the physicists have known sin; and this is a knowledge which they cannot lose."

It is one, though, that we can keep in mind as we work, and as we teach.

Go in peace.

Figure 5: You may wonder how one comes up with expressions like "root mean square." Personally, I make up a buzzword table like the one below, which is designed to be used with three dice. Suppose I roll a 342; using the table in the obvious fashion, I construct the phrase "inverse binomial fluctuation." This phrase can be used whenever I want to give the impression that I have a good handle on what is going on: "Students may find some difficulty with the apparatus in this section due to the inverse binomial fluctuation in the coils. Ask your TA for advice." The expression "root mean square" was constructed by using the roll 111 (better known as mutant snake eyes). Making up such phrases is a good way to spice up technical reports and such.

Number	Adjective 1	Adjective 2	Noun
1	root	mean	square
2	time-averaged	statistical	fluctuation
3	inverse	logarithmic	coefficient
4	correlated	binomial	relationship
5	random	gaussian	power law
6	constant	indexed	exponent

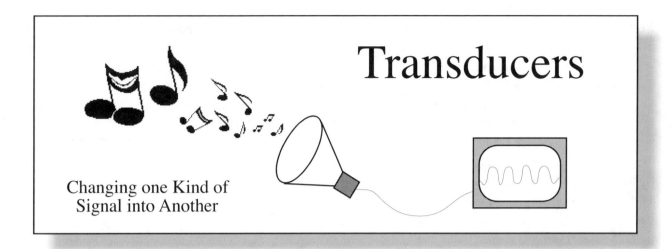

Transducers

Changing one Kind of
Signal into Another

Opening Remarks

"We need some imaginative stimulus, some not impossible ideal such as may shape vague hope, and transform it into effective desire, to carry us year after year, without disgust, through the routine work which is so large a part of life."

- Walter Pater

Exactly which role the physics lab plays in all of this—the imaginative stimulus or the routine work—will be left up to you. The basic idea of this quote is transformation: changing hope into effective desire. And this is the basic idea of this lab. (Transformation, that is, not hope or desire.)

"Transducer: A device by means of which energy can flow from one or more transmission systems to one or more other transmission systems."

- Van Nostrand's Scientific Encyclopedia

For instance, your eyes are transducers: they allow light to be converted into electrical impulses which are processed by your nervous system.

This is the theme of today's lab; the content is, however, physics. More specifically, the content is the physical principles that you have learned to this point in your physics course. Each of the transducer systems that you will look at embodies one or more of the basic electrical and/or magnetic principles we have been exploring. So this lab is a chance to review some of the basic ideas, and a chance to see some applications of the concepts we

have been learning, to answer the burning question, "But what is all of this good for?"

As you are going through the lab, think of practical uses for the different devices that you will be using. Enjoy!

Necessary Theory

There are three different types of transducers we will explore in today's lab. They are briefly described in the following sections. Each of the transducers is a way of transforming some environmental stimulus into an electrical signal that can be measured by an electrical device—such as the DMM's that you have been using in the lab.

Piezoelectric Effect

In lab you will use piezoelectric sensors which are designed more or less as follows: a sandwich of piezoelectric plastic between two metal contacts.

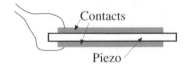

The plastic in the middle has some particular properties that make it noteworthy:

- If the plastic is deformed, it will develop a voltage across it.

- If a voltage is put across the plastic, it will deform.

112

Figure 1: Your body is full of many different kinds of transducers. Your nervous system transmits and processes electrical/chemical signals; external signals are converted into this form by your senses. The retina in your eye converts light into nerve impulses; your ears convert sound, your skin converts temperature and force, and your nose and tongue convert chemical signals. Of course, all of this sensing uses energy, which is why you must convert food energy into a form that is usable by your body, by eating and digestion. You may not eat in the lab; you may, however, digest - as long as you do it quietly.

Figure 2: Can you spot three transducers in this picture?

The piezo sensor thus will work in two complementary fashions:

- The voltage of the piezo will vary in response to a deformation of the plastic, changing a mechanical signal to an electrical one. The deformation can be very slight; we will be able to use the piezo as, for instance, a microphone.

- If an AC voltage is applied to the piezo, it will develop an AC deformation: an electrical signal is converted into a mechanical one. The deformation is slight, but we will find that the piezo can make an effective loudspeaker.

Pyroelectric Effect

The piezoelectric material discussed above is extremely versatile, as you might expect. It also has an additional mode of operation that we can explore: pyroelectricity. A small change in the temperature of the sample can produce a change in the voltage across it. The plastic has a very small heat capacity, and, as it turns out, strongly absorbs infrared radiation. Thus it can sense hot objects from a distance by changing temperature from absorbing emitted infrared. The manufacturers of the plastic we will be using claim that it can reliably detect the presence of a person 50 feet away! This takes some fancy circuit work, as you might expect, but a sample can easily detect the infrared radiation from objects that are hot but not visibly glowing.

Clamp-on Current Meter

A clamp-on current meter is a device that looks very magical. It allows you to measure AC currents without breaking a circuit or making any electrical contact. You take the meter, which has a set of pincer jaws, and clamp the jaws around a wire. The meter doesn't have to touch the wire, and the wire can be insulated. The meter will tell you the AC current flowing in the wire.

These meters are useful for measuring the power into AC appliances. You know the voltage of the appliance (115 V); if you know the current, this gives you the power. You can make the current measurement without breaking the circuit or touching any wires. And you can look at how the current changes when you adjust the appliance in different ways.

You will get a chance to make such AC current measurements in the lab. There are two goals:

i) To figure out how this baby works.

ii) To measure the power used by a heater, a computer, and other devices in the lab.

The second is very easy; we don't have to disconnect anything, and there is no chance of shock. It's the first part that's the trick. Just two words: Faraday's Law.

Photoresistor

A photoresistor does what it sounds like it should: it changes its resistance in response to a change in light intensity. You will use one of these with a DMM, and you will also get a chance to use one in a circuit that gives a voltage out that is proportional to the resistance. This will allow you to collect data for the variation on your computer; you will thus be able to measure time-varying light intensities, such as the 60 Hz variation of the light from the room lights, or the variation in light intensity from your computer screen (you can in this fashion measure the refresh rate of the screen).

The physics of how this type of device works is not that hard to figure out; given the model of conduction that you will discuss in class, you might want to give this some thought as you use it.

Experiments and Calculations

Equipment

There are three parts to this experiment, as detailed in your lab manual. All sets of equipment will need to be shared; there are not eight sets of each experiment. Consideration, civility, and a certain amount of patience with other lab groups will be necessary.

Piezoelectric Crystal

You will need the following equipment for this part:

> Piezoelectric disk unit
> Mounted piezoelectric film unit
> Meguro digital multimeter
> Oscilloscope

The piezoelectric disk units are rugged units with the piezoelectric plastic between two conductors mounted on a sturdy support. Identify this unit, and try this: connect a wire across the contacts to the piezo. Press down with a force of about 5 N with your thumb on the center of the top plate. Keep your thumb in place, and remove the wire. Stressing the crystal makes a voltage appear across it; the wire allows charges to flow from one side of the crystal to the other. Now take your thumb away. The charges stay on the crystal, and the electric field that they make will keep the crystal deformed. Place your ear near the crystal, and connect the two terminals together again. Did you hear the click? The crystal relaxed when the charges were drained off!

Next connect the piezo disk to your voltmeter. Place a mass on the disk; what happens to the voltage reading? Now take the mass off; what happens to the voltage reading now?

PUZZLE

Can you explain what is happening? Why does the voltage go to zero, then behave as it does when the mass is taken off? See if you can explain this. A hint: think capacitors (the piezoelectric crystal) and resistors (the multimeter).

The piezoelectric film unit you will use has been mounted on a plastic cup. It turns out that this will make an effective microphone: the cup works to amplify sound waves into a decent mechanical distortion—it is working as a transducer also! This distortion produces a voltage on the piezo; the piezo will be connected to the oscilloscope. Talk into the cup, and watch the display. What do you observe? How about if you tap the cup? Turn

up the sensitivity on the scope; how small a sound can you measure? (This may be a moot question in our rather noisy lab room.)

The above demonstration showed the piezo being used to change a strain into a voltage. It will also work in the reverse fashion—thus this microphone will also work as a speaker. You can show this by connecting the leads of the disk unit (the first one you used) to a signal generator, then applying a signal. Do you get some sound out? For what range of frequencies do you get the best results? Do you find that you can't hear the output below some frequency? Part of this may be due to the lack of sensitivity of your ears at low frequencies, but it is also true that these units are just too small and have too little deformation to put out good bass. Note: these units are like the ones that are used to make speakers in those cheesy musical greeting cards.

Clamp-on Current Meter

The equipment for this part consists of the meter itself:

> Clamp-on current meter

and a bunch of electrical devices on which to experiment:

> DC source connected to resistor and meter
> AC source connected to resistor and meter
> Lamp
> Fan (high and low settings)
> Soldering iron (high and low settings)
> Binary clock

First, you should verify the operation of the device. Clamp the meter around one wire in the AC circuit; compare the reading that you get on the normal ammeter to the one you get on the clamp-on meter. Now do this with the DC circuit. So: this puppy doesn't work with DC. This should give you a hint as to how it works.

PUZZLE

Describe how you think this device works. Some hints: think flux. Changing flux. Could you think of this thing as working

115

like a transformer in some way? You can get some ideas from looking at how this device works in different circumstances. For instance: what happens when you clamp the meter around two wires in the AC circuit? (Depends.) Does the sense of the wires matter? (Yep.) How about if you wrap the wire a few times around one of the jaws before closing them?

Once you have done some investigation as to how this unit works, you can put it to use measuring currents in different consumer electronic devices provided. There will be a spot in each of the power cords where you can connect to only on wire. Given that the voltage of all of the units you are looking at is 120 V rms, you can calculate the power to run each of them. (Some of the devices have a high and low setting too.) The devices might have a rating on them; you can also make a comparisons with these values. Note that the rating should be too high, if anything; these are intended to be maximum values. Some devices may well operate at well below their rated current and power. Something else to note: motors draw more current right when they are turned on, as the motor has not yet developed a back emf. So you tend to blow circuit breakers right when things are turned on—not after some time—or when a shaft seizes up so the motor can no longer turn. Can you see this effect with the motor in the fan?

As a final step, sit back and reflect quietly for a few moments on the essential neatness of this device.

Photoresistor

For this experiment, you will need the following equipment:

> Photoresistor in mount
> Mounted resistor
> 5V power supply
> Digital multimeter
> Various light sources:
>> Room lights
>> Desk lamp
>> Sun
> Macintosh computer, ULI interface

As a first step, connect the photoresistor up to your DMM, which should be set to measure resistance. The photoresistor is mounted at the base of the unit you have been given; a lens focuses light on its active area. This means that the unit is very directional: it will primarily measure light from whatever source it is aimed at.

Cover the aperture of the photoresistor; what is the "dark" resistance? Now aim it directly at the lamp you have been given; what do you measure for the "light" resistance? This gives you an idea of the range over which it will work. Try other sources of light: light from the window, light from the ceiling lamps, etc. Please do not aim the unit right at the sun.

The unit could be used in this way to measure average light intensities of different sources, and this is useful. The response time of the resistor is very rapid, though, and it can be used to measure fluctuations that are too fast for you to see. How about the room lights? They are run by AC current; thus, they should be "off" 120 times per second. How about the glow from the computer screen? It is characterized by a certain refresh rate; if you move a finger up and down in front of the screen, you can see that there is a clear strobe effect. In order to make such measurements, connect the photoresistor in the following circuit, connecting the leads to the computer as shown.

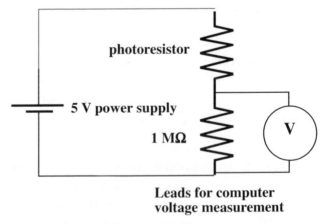

**Leads for computer
voltage measurement**

PREDICTION

Explain how this circuit works: what should happen to the voltage if the light intensity rises? If it falls?

116

Start Data Logger with the given parameters, and make some tests. Does the voltage vary as you expected? Measure some AC sources; you can play around with the data collection rate for best effect. You can use the FFT option on the analyze data screen to figure out what frequency or frequencies you have present in your varying signal; your instructor will have details. Do you see what you expect?

Summing Up

In this lab, you explore the operation of different transducers: these convert sound, light, force, and other environmental quantities into easily measurable electrical quantities. The utility of such devices in the practice of science is obvious; they are central to any measurement system.

I have no pithy comments to make at this point, so I will share with you the following calculus joke.

Q. What do mathematicians say when epsilon goes to zero?

A. There goes the neighborhood!

Go in peace.

Electromagnetic Waves...

...other than visible light

Opening Remarks

"Dr. Valman, I learned a great deal from you at the University... about the violet ray, the ultra violet ray — that you said was the highest color in the spectrum. You were wrong."

- Henry Frankenstein, from the original 1931 *Frankenstein* movie

In the 1800's the connections among life, electricity, and electromagnetic waves were a source of much speculation. Electricity could make a frog's leg jump, long after the demise of the frog. Light - and other "rays" - could give sustenance to plants and animals. A certain amount of sun exposure was found to be necessary to prevent certain diseases, for instance. And the higher energy forms of radiation were especially intriguing, as they were more penetrating. When x-rays were found, it was discovered that they could go clear through a person's body, and folks immediately set out to use them not only to diagnose diseases, but to cure them. When Mary Shelley wrote her book in 1831, she knew of electricity and ultraviolet, but it was not until the end of her century and the start of the 1900's that x-rays and gamma rays were known. In the movie there is talk of "biological galvanism" but it was a "ray" that gave Frankenstein's monster life.

In this lab, you won't bring anything to life, but you will have a chance to explore the properties of electromagnetic waves in different parts of the spectrum.

Necessary Theory

EM Waves: Nature

An electromagnetic wave is made up of oscillating electric and magnetic fields. The waves are transverse; in the case of a radio wave, the electric field is vertical.

EM Waves: Spectrum

All electromagnetic waves travel at the same speed - the speed of light - and are made of up oscillating electric and magnetic fields. They differ in their frequencies and wavelengths. At the long wavelength, low frequency end we have radio waves, which may be many meters long; at the short wavelength, high frequency end we have gamma rays, which may have wavelengths smaller than the nucleus of an atom. In between there is a range of other EM waves: microwaves, infrared, visible light, ultraviolet and x-rays. Waves at the radio end of the spectrum tend to look like waves: their electric and magnetic fields, oscillating as they do, produce the effects we see. Our experience of light and other EM waves toward the middle of the spectrum is much different, and at the far end - the x-rays and gamma rays - they look more like particles than waves in some sense.

In this lab, you will have the chance to explore the properties of many different kinds of electromagnetic waves. As you do so, note the differences - and the similarities - of the different types.

Figure 1: Radio towers give off radio waves - which are electromagnetic waves that actually carry energy. When I was a kid, I made a crystal radio that picked up radio signals with nothing more than a diode, a coil, a capacitor, and an antenna. There was no battery. I was young enough that it took me a long time to realize why this was cool: I was running a radio off the energy in the radio waves themselves! The coolest case I ever saw of this was a WWII scheme that soldiers in Europe used to make a radio out of wire, a razor blade, and a straight pin - and an earphone. It sounds like it shouldn't work, but it can - especially if you are near to a radio tower. And if you are near enough you really can - in principle - pick up radio reception on your fillings.

Figure 2: The electromagnetic spectrum. All of these waves travel at the same speed, but they have different wavelengths and frequencies.

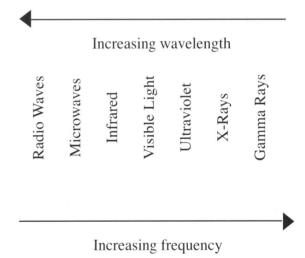

Experiments and Calculations

Equipment Needed

Each lab group will receive:

> AM radio, cut away to allow view of the ferrite bar AM antenna
> Black and white video camera, connected to computer or monitor
> Infrared source (remote control)
> Ultraviolet source (blacklight)

In addition, there will be equipment to be shared among the different lab groups:

> Thermal imaging cameras (4)
>
> Cheap and not-so-cheap sunglasses
> Different pieces of glass, filters

The thermal imaging cameras are very sensitive pieces of equipment that must be used with certain precautions. They are also irreplaceable, so please be careful with them.

119

In this lab, you will also have the chance to work in other areas than the lab. As you look for sources of radio waves and infrared, you may feel free to use the elevator, to go outside, to go to the basement, or to go to other buildings. Basically, feel free to explore - but do so with a purpose.

AM Radio Antenna: The Ferrite Bar

Check out your radio; it should have been operated on so that you can clearly see the ferrite bar that the radio uses for AM reception. This bar is designed to pick up the magnetic fields of AM radio signals - the antenna necessary to pick up the electric field component would simply be too long.

QUESTION

Explain how the ferrite bar antenna works: how is the changing magnetic field of the AM radio wave picked up by the antenna? Think about how the field would magnetize the ferrite bar, and how this would change the flux through the coil of wire wrapped around the bar - and how this would make a voltage across it.

Tune the radio to an AM station that comes in clearly, but not too strong. Move to the middle of the room, away from the metal frame desks. Now rotate the radio about a vertical axis, slowly, like so:

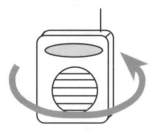

Which orientation gives the strongest signal? The weakest?

PUZZLE

Given the variation that you have observed, where is the radio station? Make a diagram to explain how the electric and magnetic fields are oriented for a wave coming from some direction, and how the radio would be turned in order to best and worst detection.

Try several radio stations; do the locations you note agree with where the stations are really coming from?

PREDICTION

Tune the radio to a station, and turn it so that you get decent reception. Suppose you were to rotate the radio about a horizontal axis like so:

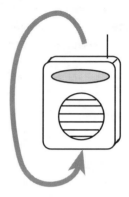

Would the signal fade at some points, or would you always receive a signal? Think about it, make a prediction, and then test.

AM Radio Waves: Other Sources

Radio waves (and generally EM waves) are produced by accelerating charges. Given this, you should be able to detect radio waves from devices that accelerate charges: devices in which currents switch on and off, say, or devices in which electron beams are moved back and forth.

Think about what sort of devices around the building might well give off radio waves. Now use your radio to test. Set the radio to AM, and vary the orientation of the radio and the tuning. Try to tune to static... but cool sounding static. Feel free to explore other labs and areas of the building.

QUESTION

What devices do you find that give off a significant amount of radio waves? Can you explain why?

FM Radio Waves: Shielding

We have seen that radio waves - being made of electric and magnetic fields - cannot go through conductors.

PUZZLE

Where in the building might you be able to find a spot that does not get FM radio reception? Think about this, and keep in mind that if you hold the radio in your hand, you are acting as an antenna - so even if you reach the radio into a spot in which it won't get reception, if your hand is touching it and you are in a spot where the waves can still reach, it will pick up the signal via your body. You should also keep in mind that the waves can penetrate a short distance.

Think of a place or two in the building to test. Are you able to find a spot in the building in which you don't get reception?

Ultraviolet: Beyond the Violet

Ultraviolet is the part of the spectrum with frequencies just above that of visible light. Ultraviolet behaves like visible light for the most part, but individual photons have more energy - and so UV rays (as we call them) can cause cellular damage. For this reason, your body develops systems to help deal with UV exposure. The most notable system is the pigment that your skin develops to protect against UV. People with dark skin are well-adapted to sunny climates: the pigment in their skin absorbs the UV before it can cause damage. But UV also serves a beneficial function in that UV exposure allows the body to synthesize vitamin D in the skin, so folks whose ancestors came from cold, cloudy climates have lighter skin - so that more UV will reach deeper layers of the skin. This also means that UV can cause changes in deeper layers of the skin - freckles and other pigmentation changes, and, in extreme cases, sunburn.

In this part of the lab, you will work with a black and white security camera that has the benefit of being sensitive to frequencies beyond the normal visible spectrum - it is sensitive well into the UV range.

For this part of the lab, you will need to have the lights in the room darkened.

Get a picture from your video camera on your video monitor or computer. With the room dark, you shouldn't see much. Now turn on the UV source (the "black light") that you have been given. Set it below the camera, and position one of your group members in front of the camera so that they are illuminated by the UV source:

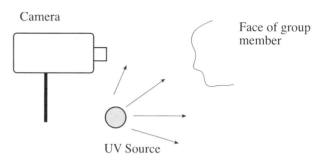

Now, notice things about their appearance. You will certainly observe fluorescence; certain things will emit visible light in the presence of UV. For instance, laundry detergent has compounds in it that stay behind in clothing, and cause whites to glow with a bluish cast. But you are mainly interested in things that are *not* glowing that the camera picks up. The person in front of the camera is illuminated with UV; it is the reflected UV that the camera picks up. In essence, you are seeing how they look in UV, which is different than how they look in visible light. Some things you might notice:

• Glasses. UV exposure to the eyes can cause deterioration of the eyes, especially cataracts. Long-term studies of people who work on fishing boats show that those who wear sunglasses or hats regularly are much less likely to develop cataracts as they age. So these days almost all eyeglasses come with an anti-UV coating. This strongly absorbs UV, and so glasses will generally appear black. How about sunglasses? Most sunglasses absorb UV also - but not all of them! Ones that don't are actually dangerous, as a person's eyes can get exposed to more UV wearing the glasses than without, since their pupils will dilate.

• Skin pigment. Folks with dark skin will show up as very dark under UV. This is because melanin, the pigment that makes skin dark, is designed to absorb UV - and so it is darker in UV than it is in visible light. Folks who tan easily will show up dark also. Folks who do not tan easily will generally show up with lots of freckles - many more than can be seen in visible light. These features that don't show up under regular illumination are real - it is just that you can

121

only see them under this special illumination. Scars generally show up as white. What other features do you note. Try other group members to see what you observe. List what observations you make, and what conclusions you draw. Think about your skin pigment as protecting your skin from UV damage as you make conclusions.

• Hair. Gray hair generally shows up as dark - a fact that I appreciate. Even though the lost pigment makes the hair appear gray, there are still pigments that absorb UV. Why is this a good thing? Note: is the same thing true for bleached or dyed hair? Do you notice any trends?

• Teeth. Teeth weakly fluoresce, but caps and other dental work generally don't.

• Colors. Check out the colors of patterns on your clothes; some will show up the way you expect; others won't.

• Sunscreen. If folks have sunscreen on, this can show up in one of two ways. Some sunscreens absorb UV - and so will appear as making skin or lips darker. Some sunscreens reflect UV - and so will show up as making skin or lips lighter. Sunscreen will, at the least, cover up details - all the freckles that you see will no longer show up.

Note: the UV lamps do emit UV. The level is not large enough to tan you or burn you, or to injure your eyes. But if you are very sensitive to UV, you should limit your exposure.

Near Infrared: Beyond the Red, But Just a Bit

Infrared - or IR - lies at frequencies below the red. Your eyes are not sensitive to IR, but the camera you used for UV is. Generally, IR is associated with heat; things which emit radiant heat are really emitting a lot of IR. IR photons have very low energy, so they won't cause cellular changes; the worst they will do is heat things up.

Near IR works pretty much like light, but with some differences: a lot of things which appear dark in visible light tend to reflect or absorb it. We can see this, but in order to get a good handle on it, we will need to get an IR source....

The IR source we will use is a remote control. Re-

mote controls emit a strong beam of IR. Point your remote control at your camera, and see what you see: you should note two light emitting diodes flashing brightly. This is a signal that is detected by a TV, VCR or other consumer device. (Note: the computer you use may well have an IR port on the front. If this is true, as you play with the remote you may well cause your computer to do things you were not expecting.)

PUZZLE

Can you imagine why manufacturers would use a beam of IR - which you can't see - rather than a beam of visible light - which you can see - to control TVs and such? (Hint: think about interference.)

Now, use the IR source as you used the UV source: to light up someone in front of the camera:

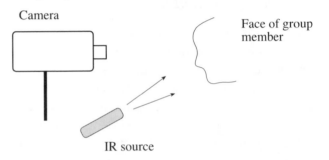

Notice how they appear in this sort of illumination. (Note: the room must be very, very dark for this to work; the camera is not very sensitive to IR, so you must be sure to reduce the background as much as possible.) Try different group members, and record your observations. Some things to note:

• Glasses. Some sunglasses absorb IR, and some do not. It turns out that sunglasses that are dark but don't absorb IR are quite bad: they make your pupils open wide, and if lots of IR comes in it could cause dangerous heating of the retina. Cheap sunglasses are often reasonably bad at absorbing IR, as are many black plastics. Note the cover on the remote! It is opaque, but the IR goes right through it. Black plastic garbage bags will let the IR through as well.

• Skin pigment. How does your skin appear? How about other group members? How does this compare with what you observed for the case of UV?

• Hair. Most hair generally shows up as white - or at least lighter than it is. Can you imagine why having hair that reflects IR would be a good thing? (Hint: imagine being outside all day, without a hat, in the hot sun.)

• Colors. Check out the colors of patterns on your clothes. You will generally find that colors dyed into cotton don't show up at all. Most cotton dyes are transparent to IR, which is interesting. What other trends do you note?

• Sunscreen. Does sunscreen have any effect on IR?

Note: in this case and in the previous case of UV, you may well find things we have not seen before. If you do, please let someone know! If it's cool enough, we will make it part of the lab in the future.

Far Infrared: Way Beyond the Pale

Any warm object will emit electromagnetic waves, primarily IR; the warmer the object, the more IR. This is far IR - it's way beyond the range that your eyes or the camera can see. But we have some IR cameras that detect the IR that you emit - as dim as it is. What these cameras will show is temperature: warm objects will appear brighter than cool objects.

There are two adjustments that you can make on the camera:

i) Brightness. If the room is cool, you will need to crank the brightness up, as there is simply not that much IR around.

ii) Contrast. The contrast will be the difference in brightness between warm and cool objects. If you turn the contrast up, you will see smaller temperature differences - but you may wash out details.

You can also adjust the focus of the camera.

Each member of your group should work on this part of the experiment; it is one that everyone should have a chance to see directly. It works best in the dark, though there can be some light in the room. Please keep the cameras turned off when not in use, and do not use them outside during the day.

Look around the room to see what objects are warm, and what objects are cool. Some things to note:

• Transformers. Transformers do lose energy in their coils; as a consequence, they will glow somewhat, as will the parts on the computers near the power supplies. There are a lot of power packs around the room that you can spot.

• Studs in the walls. If it is cool outside, if you get up close to a wall and jack up the contrast, you may well be able to pick out the studs (which are metal and will conduct heat away from the wall) as cooler, darker vertical stripes. In fact, this is what the cameras were made for: to help detect heat loss.

• Windows. The windows should be very dark compared to the walls around them.

• Clothing. People emit IR; most of what you will see in the room is people. But different kinds of clothing absorbs IR better or worse, or even insulate well enough that a person may appear dark - even though their body is warm inside their clothing. Look at different people, and note what trends you observe. (Note: these devices will not let you look at people through their clothing. Their resolution is low enough that it wouldn't be that exciting anyway.)

What other things do you note that are bright or dark? Record your observations.

Summing Up

The image of Dr. Frankenstein, laughing wildly in his lab with the electric discharges, is one that is pretty well part of our culture. There is this enduring image of the mad scientist: a crazed loner who does experiments that are ethically suspect or longs for world domination. In fact, most scientists are pretty boring people, and they generally want to help people. Scientists do get obsessed, and they do work long hours, but labs are generally a lot more boring (and a lot less well-appointed) than they appear in the movies. When I was in grad school and I took my girlfriend to my lab, she said, "This is it?" I think she was expecting crazy electrical discharges and computer screens with fancy graphics. Instead, I was doing an experiment in a fish tank surrounded by blue board, with the results read out on a strip chart recorder. It was a cool experiment, but it didn't look like it. I am happy to report, though, that she married me anyway. As in many cases, reality is a lot less interesting on the surface than the movies, but when you dig a bit, you might find that it is more interesting than you expected.

Go in peace.

Reflection and Refraction

Bouncing and Bending Light

Opening Remarks

The reflection and refraction of light have been well studied since antiquity. Mirrors have existed for many thousands of years, and people fishing with spears have always been aware that where the fish looks to be is not where he is—refraction alters the view.

The Greeks did quite a bit of work on optics. They were aware of the mathematical principles of reflection and refraction, and they had even worked out a justification of the law of reflection, as noted in the caption to Figure 1. The principle of minimum distance does not explain refraction, obviously, but by minimizing the time for the path one can derive Snell's Law. Similar "minimum principles" apply in many branches of physics, and can be a very powerful technique.

In this lab you will have a chance to explore the properties of reflection and refraction. The lab is intended to be somewhat open-ended; feel free to explore.

Necessary Theory

The Ray Box

In this lab, we will use as our basic system a ray box that can produce parallel or diverging rays of light that can be acted on by different optical elements. The ray box projects rays along the table;

the elements are all designed to have flat bottoms, so you will be able to trace the rays directly by placing a sheet of paper under the system. You can thus make real-life ray diagrams. You will use these ray diagrams to verify and explore certain principles that you will see in class. To give you an idea as to the material covered, you will explore such topics as:

Reflection: The Plane Mirror

By tracing the rays, you can show where the image in a mirror appears.

Reflection: Concave and Convex Mirrors

You will have concave and convex mirrors that you can use to show how these elements focus or diverge rays of light. You can identify the focal points for these elements.

Refraction: The Prism

You can show how the rays of light are diverted by a prism, and you can show how the light is spread into a spectrum.

Refraction: Total Internal Reflection

You can use a 45° prism to show how light is totally internally reflected in a prism. This is how the reflectors in binoculars work; we will have such prisms available for your inspection. You can also measure the critical angle, and thus determine the index of refraction.

124

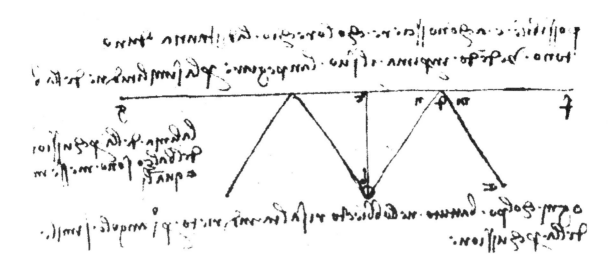

Figure 1: A rather poor copy of an early text by Leonardo da Vinci showing his elucidation of the law that the angle of reflection is equal to the angle of incidence. Leonardo first deduced this rule for projectiles rebounding from flat surfaces, as in the diagram. He then applied this rule to the different wave phenomena that he studied, such as light. Leonardo was not the first person to deduce this rule; the Greeks were well aware of it, and could show that this was the path of least distance. (Work it out! To get between any two points by a reflection, this is the shortest path.) You will also note that the above writing looks odd; if you hold it up to a mirror (for instance, the one you will use in lab), you will be able to see why. (You still won't be able to read it, unless you read Italian.) Leonardo, besides being a genius (as a painter, architect, engineer, scientist, and man of letters), was a bit paranoid, and he wrote his notes in mirror writing or otherwise encrypted them. Try writing like this some time; it's no wonder that his penmanship was so poor.

Refraction: Lenses

You will have a variety of different lenses to try out. You can see how they affect the rays, how they converge or diverge them, measure focal points, and measure such effects as chromatic and spherical aberration.

Refraction: Lens Systems

By combining the lenses you have, you can make different lens systems and show, for example, such things as how corrective lenses aid vision, how a telescope works, and so on.

Color Mixing

In addition to all of the above, the ray box comes with a system of colored filters and mirrors that you can use to explore the mixing of different colors of light. You can explore additive and subtractive spectra. Do the primary colors really mix to make white light? Give it a try!

Experiments and Calculations

Equipment

Each group will be provided with the following equipment:

> Black ray box
> 12 V power supply
> Tray of lenses, blocks, mirrors
> Colored slides and squares
> Paper for recording rays, etc.
> Protractor
> Clear ruler

The ray boxes have a 12 V bulb that is run by the power supply; one end of the box has a set of slits, the other some rotatable mirrors. The light from the slits is projected so that rays can be seen on a piece of paper that the box is placed on. An adjustment on the top of the box can make the rays parallel. These rays can then be reflected, refracted, split into colors, and so on by the collection of optical elements you have been given. The end of the box with mirrors has three slide holders in which the colored slides can be placed. If the three holders are used with three slides, the mirrors allow you to reflect the different colors of light to mix them on white paper to see the result

Some cautions to observe:

> • Turn the ray box off when not in use. These things get hot!

> • Keep the optical elements in the tray provided.

> • Handle the optical elements by the handles provided or by the edges. Otherwise you will leave fingerprints on the edges that will interfere with their performance.

> • You will get the best results from your ray box if you set the knob on the top so that the rays that come out are nearly parallel.

It is especially important that you use care with the optical elements. We can only buy them as a set, so be sure to keep them in the tray and handle them with care.

Reflection

We have a collection of mirrors that you can use, of varying degrees of curvature:

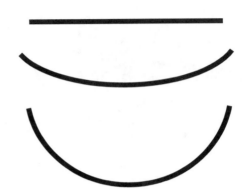

Some things that you may wish to explore with them are noted below. Use a piece of paper to record the paths of the rays. Make sketches of what you see so that your lab manual is a good record of what you have done.

• Consider the plane mirror. Does the angle of incidence equal the angle of reflection?

PUZZLE

For the plane mirror, can you show why the image is reversed? How do you show this with ray diagrams? What does it mean for the image to be reversed?

• For the less curved mirror, measure the focal length on the concave side, and the convex side if you can. Do the numbers agree? Make a rough measurement of the radius of curvature; is this consistent with the focal length you measured? (What is the expression relating the two?)

PUZZLE

For the less curved mirror (concave side), show, using ray diagrams, where you get inverted and non-inverted images. How is this related to the focal point?

• For the more curved mirror, look at the reflection from the concave side. Measure the focal point. Now set the rays so that they are off center; can you get a single focus now? The segment of mirror you have is cylindrical; for it to focus from any point on the mirror, it would have to be parabolic. Thus, off-axis rays don't come to focus at the proper point. This is what is knows as a spherical aberration; see the makers of the Hubble Space Telescope for more details.

You can also do internal reflection from a block. The case that is particularly of note is the corner reflector:

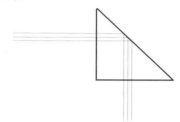

Note that all of the light is reflected. This is the type of reflector that is used in binoculars; can you think of any reason why it might be superior to a mirror?

PUZZLE

Why is the light reflected from the inside surface? Can you have a situation where some of the light is reflected and some not? What is meant by the term "critical angle"?

Refraction

In addition to the block noted above, you have several other shapes of plastic block to explore:

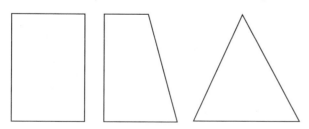

The blocks are rough on one side; if this side is placed down, you can see the rays as they traverse the blocks. As you work with the blocks, do your measurements on a piece of paper. You can then trace the paths of the rays, which will facilitate quantitative measurements. A question: how can you record the path of a ray inside the block? Recall that two points define a line.

Some investigations you should do with one or more of these blocks:

• Play with the blocks to see what each of them does.

• Determine the index of refraction of the blocks. Do this two ways for one block:

i) Measure the angle of incidence and the angle of refraction, and use Snell's Law. Try a few angles, and average your results for n.

ii) Measure the critical angle beyond which all light is internally reflected. This will also give a value for n. (Something to note: the critical angle may vary for different colors!) (Note: you can't do this with a rectangular block. Why not?)

Do your two results agree?

• Try to use a prism (or two!) to get a good rainbow pattern.

Lenses

The kit you will get has three lenses that you can use:

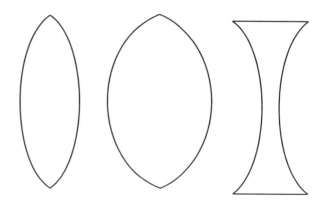

• Measuring from the center of each lens, measure the focal length for each. (How do you measure the focal length for a diverging lens?)

Set up the case of the Galilean telescope:

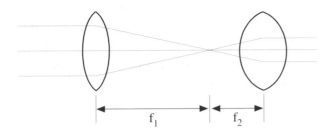

The rays that come out are still parallel (as from a distant object), but closer together. What happens to rays that come in at an angle?

PUZZLE

Can you explain how this allows the telescope to magnify? You may want to talk to your instructor about this one.

Next, use the thickest lens as a model of the eye. In your eye, the image should form on the retina, but it does not in all people.

PUZZLE

Use the two other lenses (one concave, one convex) with this lens (which plays the role of your eye's lens) to show how glasses are used to correct nearsightedness and farsightedness. Make ray diagrams to show your results. Which lens is used for which condition?

Colors

Color mixing is really an art rather than a science. Artist friends of mine know much better than I what colors are complementary to each other and such things; what we see as individual colors are not single wavelengths or even simple mixes of wavelengths. Mixing the primary colors of light to make white light may not reconstitute the entire spectrum, but makes a mix of wavelengths that we will see as white. What do you get when you mix red and green? The result might surprise you!

Use the different colored slides in the holders provided, and then use the mirrors to mix beams of different colors. Do you notice any trends? Your instructor will have some advice. You may also

want to illuminate the colored squares of cardboard with light of different colors to see how they appear in different colors of light.

And When You Are Done...

Put everything back where you found it. Please be courteous to the students who will follow you in lab.

Summary

In this lab you will get a chance to explore the principles of reflection and refraction. The instrument you will use, the ray box, and the optical elements, are a very nice system. Just imagine what Leonardo could have done with this kind of stuff! Maybe then he wouldn't have felt compelled to fritter away time painting the Mona Lisa and other stuff like that. Just for the record: Leonardo, in addition to his serious work and art, also wrote and performed humor for the royal court. I use this as my justification for my jocular style in this manual. I am just trying to be a Renaissance man.

Figure 2: Early ideas about the composition of the moon were rather fanciful. It was not until the advent of the Galilean telescope that the true nature of the lunar surface—rocky, mountainous, dry and airless—became known. We also know now that the silvery appearance of the earth in moonlight is due not to some peculiar property of the light, but due to the limitations of our eyes—our color vision does not work well in low light levels. Oh well; so much for romance.

Thin Lenses

Making a nice, sharp image

Opening Remarks

Humans are visual creatures: we take in vast amounts of information through the use of our eyes. But it was only recently, around the year 1600, that artificial aids to vision began to be used. Shortly after that time, Galileo turned a simple telescope consisting of two thin lenses toward the sky, and what he saw changed the way we perceived the universe.

Not everyone greeted his revelations with pleasure; Francisco Sizzi, a Professor of Astronomy, said about Galileo's discovery of Jupiter's four largest moons:

"Jupiter's moons are invisible to the naked eye and therefore can have no influence on the earth, and therefore would be useless, and therefore do not exist."

This argument has a certain perverse logic to it, you must admit. There was initially quite a bit of suspicion about the use of telescopes, microscopes and so on: people took some time to be convinced that the observations of moons and microbes were not products of the instruments, but were actual objects that merely lay beyond our perception. But, we are tool-using, visual animals, so it was inevitable that telescopes, microscopes, cameras, television and other devices would come to play large roles in our lives.

The basis of this revolution was the thin lens. And this is what you will be studying today. By itself, a lens can correct vision, make images, or serve as a magnifier; with other lenses it can make all manner of optical devices. Today's lab will give you a taste of this, plus give you a chance to work with the equations governing image formation in lens systems.

Necessary Theory

Consider a thin lens of focal length f. ("Thin" in this context means that the thickness of the lens is very much less than the focal length.) To the right of the lens we place a source of light, say a candle. To the left of the lens we place a screen. For the right placement of the three objects, an image can form. The image can be projected on a screen, and therefore must be real. It will also be inverted. The distances are as in Figure 2: f is the focal length of the lens, s is the distance from the source or object to the lens (to the center of the lens), and s' is the distance from the lens to the image. The following relationship holds among the distances:

$$\frac{1}{s} + \frac{1}{s'} = \frac{1}{f}$$

The basic lens equation above is derived using ray diagrams. Note that it will apply to other situations; there is a sign convention that will adapt it. For the situation of Figure 2, all signs are positive. This case has a *real* object (i.e. it is in front of the lens), a *real* image and a *converging* lens (which converges light rays - a convex lens.) In the case of a *virtual* object (i.e. it is in back of the lens) you

130

Figure 1: "Philosophy is written in this grand book -- I mean the universe -- which stands continually open to our gaze...." (Galileo Galilei, *Il Saggiatore*) Unfortunately, it was just this philosophy that got Galileo in trouble with the church. It was not his findings, but the philosophical impact of them — that the earth is not the center of the universe — that got him into trouble with the Inquisition. (Actually, it was also due to politics. He had made some powerful enemies in his younger years.) An example is the moons of Jupiter. If Jupiter has moons, then there is another center of orbits besides the earth. This opened the door to saying that the sun, and not the earth, was at the center of the solar system. This is why the person noted earlier was so distraught at Galileo's seemingly innocuous discovery. Under duress of a trial by the Inquisition he eventually recanted his belief that the earth moves about the sun, but supposedly made the above remark *sotto voce* immediately thereafter. It is unclear whether or not he really did this, but if a Hollywood movie is made of his life you can bet a fiery-eyed Galileo will angrily mutter something like this as he turns from his inquisitors.

E pur si muove!*

*But it does move!

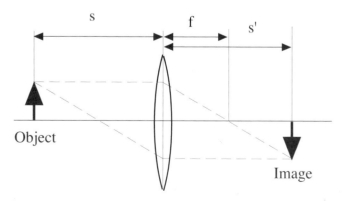

Figure 2: Object and image positions for a thin lens; note the meaning of the different distances. (The notation may differ from that in your text.) Two possible rays for locating the object are shown.

s   f   s'

Object

Image

would make s negative, For the case of a *virtual* image you would make s' negative. For a *diverging* (concave) lens, you would make f negative. You will get a chance to work with all of these cases in the lab.

For the diverging lenses, you won't be able to measure exactly where the image is. But you will be able to notice how big it is - and this will allow you to deduce its position. Recall that the magnification of the image is given by:

$$M = -\frac{s'}{s}$$

The sign gives the orientation: negative means the image is inverted, positive means it is right side up. (We could also say "uninverted," using that wacky double-negative physicist-speak that we so love. Believe it or not, this is the preferred terminology among my people.)

Given the form of the equation for the distances shown, it is often more convenient to work in terms of the power of a lens instead of the focal length. The power is defined as follows:

power (in diopters) = 1/f (f is in meters)

The reason for using this form is that for two thin lenses, the effective power is just the sum of the powers of the two lenses taken separately:

$$\frac{1}{f} = \frac{1}{f_1} + \frac{1}{f_2}$$

An example is in correcting vision. The power of the eye's lens should be about 60 diopters; suppose a person's lens has a power of only 57 diopters. This person will be farsighted. But, if they use a corrective lens, in eyeglasses or a contact lens, with a power of 3 diopters, the total power will be 60 diopters—just what it should be.

Experiments and Calculations

Necessary Equipment

Each group will have the following equipment:

Light source (night light with arrow)
Optics bench (meter stick mounted on stand)
Optics bench components:
    Two lens mounts
    Screen holder
    Screen, with ruled grid lines
    "Pointer"
    Set of 6 lenses, 4 converging and
        diverging.

The optics bench components will ride on the meter stick. Please move them back and forth carefully so that they do not scratch off the coating from the meter sticks. The lenses should be handled by the edges only; please use care putting them in and taking them out of the lens mounts.

The light source is a lamp and screen that can be positioned above a specific spot on your meter stick. There is an arrow on the end that you can focus on; this will give you a clear object position, and will also show object orientation.

Comment on Procedure

The point of doing this lab is to teach you something about lenses. And it turns out that the best way to learn about lenses is to use them to make images and to look through them. When you work with lenses and images, make sure that everyone in your group has a chance to work with the lenses and look at the images. I know that it is a common practice to subdivide the work of the lab - to say, "OK, you do this measurement, and I will do another, and then we can share information." In the real world, this is a great way to get things done, because in the real world we care about results. In this lab, though, we don't - not really. What we care about is learning, and you will learn the most if you work carefully through each of the exercises with your whole group, being sure that each member of your group has a chance to do each of the exercises.

For this lab, more than ones that have come before, there is more work to do than you can do in the time allotted, unless you rush. Don't rush; do what you can in the one hour and forty minutes of lab. Focus on what you have done, not what you haven't done.

Characterizing Your Lenses

Your first task will be to characterize the lenses that you have. The focal lengths of the lenses will be even multiples of 5 cm; you won't have a lens with a focal length of, say, 13 cm. So you can do a rough estimate of the focal length, and this will probably be good enough. To measure the focal lengths of the converging and diverging lenses, you will need to use two very different techniques:

Converging lenses. In this case, the best approach is to make an image of a distant object; as you can see from the formula above, if s is very large, s' is approximately equal to f.

CALCULATION

Sketch a ray diagram to show why this is true.

There should be a light source in the center of the lab that is far enough away from your table to serve as a distant light source; focus on it, measure the distance from the lens to the screen (which will be s') and take this to be a good approximation of the focal length.

Diverging lenses. Diverging lenses are a bit trickier; they don't make a real image whose position you can measure. You will need to deduce where the image is from where it is.

CALCULATION

Suppose a diverging lens forms an image that is exactly one-half the size of the object. Where is the image, and where is the object? Work this out, and then sketch a ray diagram to show what this situation looks like.

You can use the result of your calculation as follows: look at the ruled screen of paper you have

been given through a diverging lens. Now get well back from the lens, so that both the object (the screen) and the image seen through the lens are well back from you. Try to look at both the image and the object at the same time, so that you can compare their relative sizes. (Note: this is why it is important to be well back; if you are too close, the image, which will be closer to you, will appear larger to you than it should.) Have one of your lab partners set the positions of the lens and the screen so that the image of the screen viewed through the lens is one-half the size of the screen. Now measure the distance from the lens to the screen, and use your above result to calculate the focal length of the lens.

Once you have measured the focal lengths for all of your lenses, do one final calculation:

CALCULATION

Now that you have the focal lengths of the lenses, calculate the powers of the different lenses, in units of diopters.

Real Images

Of course, this section of the lab will use the converging lenses only!

Use each of your four different converging lenses to make an image of a distant object. Use the grid on your screen to measure the size of the image for each one.

CALCULATION

Can you come up with a relationship between the focal length (or the power) and the size of the image of a distant source?

This will be an important relationship for us to consider when we talk about optical instruments.

Next, take a single lens in the middle of the range of focal lengths available to you, and set it in the holder. Set your source some distance from the lens, and move the screen until the image is in good focus. Measure the lens-source distance and the lens-image distance.

CALCULATION

Given these values for the distances, what do you compute for the focal length of your lens, using the basic equation from the theory section? Does this agree with your estimate of the focal distance from before?

Now, adjust the position of the source, and reposition the screen so that the image is in focus. Record the lens-source distance and the lens-image distance again. Do this several times, and record your data. As you take data, sketch a graph of how the position of the image varies as you change the position of the object. Do a series of values that start far away from the focal point and then come close to it. Near the focal point, you may want to take data at a number of closely spaced points, as a small change in object distance near the focal point will make a large change in the image position. On your graph, be sure to note where the focal length is, on both axes.

Virtual Images

Converging Lenses. For one of your converging lenses, look at an object through the lens, and note the position, magnification, and orientation of the image that you see as a function of distance. How does the image appear when the object is very close to the lens? Farther away? How does the image (position, magnification and orientation) change as the distance between the object and the lens approaches the focal length? How does the image (position, magnification and orientation) change as the distance between the object and the lens goes beyond the focal length?

CALCULATION

Sketch a ray diagram showing the image position for a virtual image produced by a converging lens of an object closer to the lens than the focal point.

PUZZLE

Suppose you had to determine the focal length of a converging lens, but you had

no source to project an image of. Can you determine a way that you could estimate a focal length by looking through the lens at an object?

Diverging Lenses. For one of your diverging lenses, look at an object through the lens, and note the position, magnification, and orientation of the image that you see as a function of distance. How does the image appear when the object is very close to the lens? Farther away? How does the image (position, magnification and orientation) change as the distance between the object and the lens approaches the focal length? How does the image (position, magnification and orientation) change as the distance between the object and the lens goes beyond the focal length?

CALCULATION

Sketch a ray diagram showing the image position for a virtual image produced by a diverging lens of an object closer to the lens than the focal point.

QUESTION

What differences do you see in the virtual images formed by the converging lens and the diverging lens?

Combinations of Lenses

We have seen how two lenses, acting in concert, will act like a single lens with a power that is the sum of the powers of the two lenses.

PREDICTION

Choose two of your converging lenses, and predict what the focal length would be for the two lenses working as a pair. (Note: you will get better results if you choose two longer focal length lenses. For the short focal length ones, which are fatter, the thin lens approximation is not as good.)

Now take the two lenses, place them together, and measure the focal length of the combination. Does it have the value you predicted?

PREDICTION

Choose a converging lens and a diverging lens, and predict what the focal length would be for the two lenses working as a pair.

Now take the two lenses, place them together, and measure the focal length of the combination. Does it have the value you predicted? (Note: exactly how you measure this focal length will depend on whether you predict a positive or a negative focal length for the combination!)

Summary

The heart of this lab is a very simple exercise in making images using lenses on the optical bench. Be sure that you personally have a chance to look through the lenses and see the phenomena under discussion. For virtual images especially, only one person can look at them at a time, and if you do not take part in the observations you will miss out on a key component of the lab.

The question of how much we can believe what our instruments - such as a telescope - show us as opposed to what our eyes show us was - and is - a lively topic of debate. Is something less real because you need a telescope to see it? This is an interesting question. Ultimately, though, I tend to take a pragmatic view of these things. Jupiter's moons may not be real, but we have taken pictures of them. And that's real enough for me.

Go in peace.

Physics of Vision

Light and Color and How Your Eye Works

Introduction and Theory

"God does not care about our mathematical difficulties. He integrates empirically."

- Albert Einstein

In what follows, don't think too hard about what *should* happen; observe instead what *does* happen.

The point of today's lab is for you to learn about geometrical optics while exploring the basics of how a particular optical device works: your eye.

Since much of what you will be learning today will be based on what happens inside your eye, it is crucial that each person perform each of the experiments. You should still work as a group, but each person should try each experiment. We will have enough equipment for everyone.

Necessary Theory

What follows is some of the theory of how your eye works; additional information can be obtained from your text or from the lecture.

The basic structure of your eye works like this: a thin lens of focal length f (really the crystalline lens of your eye plus the cornea) projects the image of a source of light, say a candle, on a screen: the retina of your eye. The image is real, of course, and so is inverted. The distances are as in Figure 2: f is

the focal length of your eye's lens, s is the distance from the source or object to the lens (to the center of the lens), and s' is the distance from the lens to the image - which is the length of your eye. The following relationship - the same equation as for any thin lens - holds among the distances:

$$\frac{1}{s} + \frac{1}{s'} = \frac{1}{f}$$

The distance from the lens to the retina is fixed - and so to focus on objects at different positions, the eye changes its shape. This has the effect of adjusting f - until you reach an age at which your eye can no longer do this effectively, in which case you get reading glasses!

Given the form of the equation for the distances shown, it is often more convenient to work in terms of the power of a lens instead of the focal length. The power is defined as follows:

power (in diopters) = 1/f (f is in meters)

If you need corrective lenses, the effective power of your eye's lens plus an added lens is just the sum of the powers of your eye's lens (f_1) plus the power of the lens added to it (f_2):

$$\frac{1}{f} = \frac{1}{f_1} + \frac{1}{f_2}$$

The power of the eye's lens should be about 60 diopters; suppose a person's lens has a power of only 57 diopters. This person will be farsighted. But, if they use a corrective lens, in eyeglasses or a contact

136

Figure 1: OK, now which is better: 1 or 2? OK, how about now? 1 or 2? Good, good! How about now, 1 or 2? OK, now read the lowest line of letters that you can read clearly....

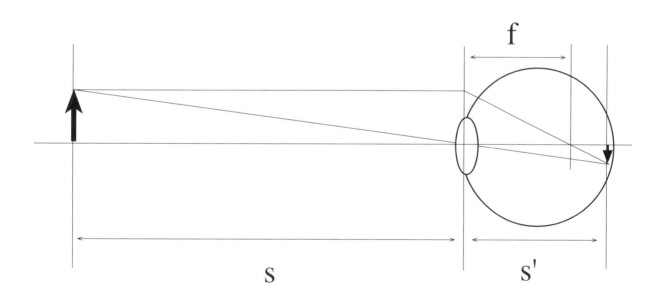

Figure 2: The basic optics of your eye are just like you have seen for a thin lens that makes a real image. It's a pretty simple optical system, really. (Note: the lens is shown as a single lens for clarity. In fact, much of the power of your eye's imaging system comes from the cornea, which is the part of your eye that is reshaped in laser vision correction.)

lens, with a power of 3 diopters, the total power will be 60 diopters—just what it should be.

Experiments and Observations

Note: the experiments and the report for this lab are to be done by *each person*. Each person should do all the experiments and record his or her own observations. But you may still feel free to work in groups.

Don't worry about "finishing" this lab; work carefully on what you do. If you wear glasses, keep them on unless advised otherwise.

Equipment Needed

Each person will receive:

Foam block
Pair of double lenses
Small ruler
3x5 Card to use as screen
Cardboard cutout shape
Wax paper in holder
Film canister with lens on one end, rubber dam on other
Pinhole viewer
Disk with Color Mixing widget
Set of colored slides
Pair of matched optical front-mounted sensing devices

Please keep track of all parts; there are a lot of them!

Lenses: Real Images

You will recognize the double lens as a magnifying glass. There are two lenses, of two different sizes.

Place your 3x5 card on the table, and hold the large lens above it. Move the lens until an image (of the lights in the ceiling) forms. Measure the distance from the card to the lens; this is the focal length of the lens. What is the focal length in centimeters? (Don't even think about using inches!)

Next, do the same thing with the small lens.

CALCULATION

Compute the power of both lenses, in diopters.

Now go to a window and use the large lens to project an image of something outside the building onto your card screen. What do you notice about the image on the card?

Now project the same image with the small lens. Is the image bigger or smaller than the image from the large lens?

QUESTION

Which makes a larger image: a short focal length lens, or a long focal length lens?

DERIVATION

Can you show why one lens makes a larger image than the other? Do this.

Now, try this: set up the larger of the two lenses to make an image. Now place the cardboard cutout right in front of the lens. How does this affect the image? Is this what you expected?

Lenses: Virtual Images

If you look through a lens and an image does not form, we say that there is a *virtual* image. This is the usual way to use a magnifying glass.

For each person in your group, do the following measurements and calculations. If you wear glasses, keep them on for now.

Look through one eye at this page. How close can you get to the page, looking with one eye, and still keep the image in *sharp* focus? Measure this distance; it is called your *near point*.

CALCULATION

Given the near point that you have measured, what is the range of focus of your eye - that is, what range of powers can your lens go to? (You may assume that 1/s' is 60 for your eye.)

If you wear glasses, repeat the above experiment and calculation - without your glasses. If you are nearsighted, you will also need to measure your far point - the greatest distance at which you can focus clearly.

Now, hold the large lens right next to your eye (very, very close; as close as a person with glasses has the lenses to their eye); this is the correct way to use a magnifying glass. Now measure your near point and far point, with the lens in front of your eye.

CALCULATION

What is the range of powers that your eye (plus the lens) can focus to now? How should this range compare to what you measured before, for your unaided eye? Does this comparison work?

Now measure your near point and far point when looking through the small lens, and do the same calculations.

Which lens allows you to get the closest (and therefore largest) view: the short focal length lens, or the long focal length lens?

The magnifying glass really works not by magnifying, but by allowing you to get very close to something, where its *apparent* size is larger.

The Telescope

A telescope consists of two lenses: one lens (the objective) makes a real image, and the other (the eyepiece) works as a magnifier to look at the image.

QUESTION

One of the goals of using a telescope is to magnify an image. Given this, which lens, the short focal length lens or the long focal length lens, should you use to project the image?

QUESTION

Now, you want to magnify this image. Which lens should you use: the short focal

length lens, or the long focal length lens?

Now build a little telescope, using the foam block.

CALCULATION

Measure the distance between the two lenses. Does it have the value that you predict it should? Compare the value you measure with the predicted value.

Look through the eyepiece and the objective at a distant object. What do you notice about the image?

To verify the operation of the telescope, place the wax paper screen in between the two lenses so that a real image is projected on the screen. Now look at the image on the screen through the eyepiece. It will be magnified. Now take the screen away. The image is the same! Explain what is going on, in terms of the operation of the telescope.

The Microscope

You can use your two lenses in the foam holder to make a microscope, by using both short focal length lenses together.

Use your two lenses to make a microscope like this, and observe its operation. Are you able to use it to look at a close object, and see it magnified significantly?

CALCULATION

Sketch a ray diagram showing the operation of a microscope. Where does the image form from the objective? How about the virtual image of this image as seen through the eyepiece?

Model of the Eye

The film canister with the lens on one side and the rubber dam on the other is a model of the human eye. Your eye has a lens on the front, and a screen (the retina) on the back.

Point the eye model at a bright object or scene, and look at the image on the screen.

CALCULATION

What do you notice about the image? Show, using a ray diagram, why the image is inverted.

QUESTION

What does this tell you about the image that is formed on your retina when you look at something?

Now, try to use the eye model to look at a very close object. (A lamp will be provided.) Can you do this and still keep the object in focus?

In order to maintain focus, you would have to change the focal length of the lens. In your eye, this is done by accommodation: muscles in the eye deform the lens to change its shape. This lens can't be changed, so we could say that it is farsighted.

Try looking at a close object using your magnifying glass as a corrective lens in front of the eye model. Can you use the eye model to focus on a close object now? Measure the distance of the object for a sharp focus.

CALCULATION

Given what you have measured for the power of the corrective lens, is this where you would predict the focus would be? Do a calculation for this model as you did for your eye. You can measure q directly, of course, and you can also deduce f.

Proof by Demo

Of course, just because someone tells you that the image of a scene is inverted on your retina is no good reason to believe it. After several weeks of Physics, we expect you to demand more proof than that. So here it is.

The pinhole viewer that you have been given has, appropriately enough, a single pinhole in one end. The pinhole will serve as a light source. At the other end of the viewer is a set of three pinholes.. The light from the pinhole will cast a shadow of the three holes.

With one eye, hold the end of the viewer with the three holes in a triangle pattern up to your eye. Now move the viewer as close as you can to your eye. Now the light source (the pinhole) is too close to focus on, as is the pattern of holes. So instead of your eye focusing an image, which would be upside down, a shadow of the holes will be projected onto your retina. The shadow will *not* be inverted. How does the triangular pattern of the holes appear? How is it actually oriented?

QUESTION

Explain why the image of the holes appears as it does.

If you are having trouble understanding this one, try this: take your eye model and the bright source of light for the close image. Put the eye model very close to the light, with the tip of a pen in between. There will be a (right-side-up) shadow of a pen tip in the screen!

No-Lens Imaging

It is possible to use the pinhole in your pinhole viewer for other purposes.

If there is sunlight coming in through a window, use your pinhole to project an image of the sun. You do this by placing the pinhole between the sun and a card on which you project an image. Even though it is not a lens, the pinhole can still project an image. Describe what you see.

A pinhole can also help a lens form a sharper image. There are two versions of the following experiment, one for people with glasses, and one for folks not lucky enough to wear them.

If you have glasses, take them off. Now look at a distant object (if you are nearsighted) or a close object (if you are farsighted). It should be out of focus. Now put the pinhole right up against your eye. What do you notice about the image now?

If you don't have glasses, make yourself nearsighted by placing the large lens of your magnifying glass in front of your eye. Now look at a distant object; it should be way out of focus. Now place the pinhole right in front of the lens. What do you notice about the image now?

You can also use the pinhole to change your near point. Place the pinhole in front of your eye, and see how close you can get to something while still keeping it in focus. Can you get closer than before?

Color Mixing

There are three primary colors: red, green, and blue. This is why color computer monitors are sometimes called "RGB." You will be given a program, which is called "Color Mixing Widget" that you can use to mix the different colors on the screen. Start up the program; you can turn on red, green and blue phosphors separately. This is *additive* color mixing: you are adding colors of light.

QUESTION

What color do you get when you mix red and green?

QUESTION

What color do you get when you mix red and blue?

QUESTION

What color do you get when you mix green and blue?

QUESTION

What color do you get when you mix red, green and blue?

You should also try mixing different amounts of the different colors, to see what different colors you can get. In principle, you can make any color this way.

QUESTION

How do you get orange? How about brown? Periwinkle?

Red, green and blue should make white. By mixing different amounts of red, green and blue you can make any color that you wish. Note that this is due to the physiology of your eye, not due to any particular principle of physics! The colors that you make by mixing two of the three primary colors are called, obviously enough, *secondary* colors.

Color Mixing II

The secondary colors are also called *complementary* colors. The three complementary colors are called cyan, magenta, and yellow. Cyan is a mix of green and blue. You have a cyan filter; you might be tempted to call it blue, but it's not: it's cyan. This filter does subtraction: it keeps out light of a certain color. The light that comes through is cyan, which is a mix of green and blue; therefore, the filter is filtering out red light. So we can also think of cyan as "not red," or the *complement* of red. This is why they are called complementary colors. For the record, yellow is "not blue," and magenta is "not green."

PREDICTION

Predict what colors you get when you put the following filter combinations together. This is subtractive color mixing; when you add a filter, you subtract a certain color.

Cyan + Yellow =

Cyan + Magenta =

Yellow + Magenta =

Now try these combinations, and see what you get. What happens if you put all three filters together?

Try looking at different colored objects through the various filters. Try to be systematic; record your observations.

Final Remarks

Much of the original work on optics was done by Isaac Newton, of Newton's Laws. He did a fair amount of experimentation with lenses and with colors. He also did a fair amount of experimentation on himself, for instance sticking a splinter in his eye to apply pressure on it, to see what effects he observed. And he looked at the sun for a long period of time and made himself blind for a while.

And, of course, due to his commitment to numerology, he added an extra color, indigo, to the spectrum, which is why you have been taught about Roy G. Biv. There is no such person. The colors of the spectrum are red, orange, yellow, green, blue and violet. But Newton wanted a seventh color, since there were seven planets and seven was a magical number.

Hey—even Isaac Newton had his off days.

Go in peace.

Those of us who are nearsighted can play some interesting optical tricks. If you are nearsighted, here's one you can try. In the evening, when you are outside, look at a distant streetlight - one far enough away that it looks like a small dot of light. Now take off your glasses. The light will now look like a circle of light. What you are seeing is an image of your pupil. Close your eye, and open it again. Does the size of the circle change? It will if your pupil's size changes! And, if you pay attention, you might see some "floaters": little bubbles and bits of stuff that float across (and inside!) your eye. There are bubbles, squiggles, and all mannner of interesting species of floaters. (Note: you can also tell if you are astigmatic. Does the shape of the circle of light appear as a true circle, or an oval? If it's an oval, you have an astigmatism!)

I used to amuse myself this way at night baseball games that my father took the family to. I used to like baseball for a few innings, but after a point, the antics of the Columbus Jets started to get a bit old. But the lights that lit up the field were cool.

If you are farsighted, this won't work. But get yourself a magnifying glass, and hold this in front of your eye. This has the effect of making you nearsighted, so you can do the same thing.

Optics of the Eye

Understanding a basic optical system

Opening Remarks

"I stuck ye bodkin well into my eye..."

- *Isaac Newton*

Before Isaac Newton's time, there was much speculation about the workings of the eye. For years, it was a common belief that the eye sent out rays of some sort that bounced off things and then returned to the eye to allow it to sense things - just as radar and sonar work. Isaac Newton did pioneering work on light as he had done on mechanics. He showed that you could break light into colors, and he explored the workings of the eye - in many cases by experimenting on himself. In one case, he stuck a small stick into his eye socket and pressed on the eyeball to observe the resulting visual sensations. He also took it upon himself to stare at the sun for some time, to see what would happen. In fact, what happened was that he lost his vision for a few days - and he was lucky that was all. Isaac Newton was a pioneer, but he was also, at times, a bit of a wacko.

Isaac Newton's particular proclivities have given us an odd bit of misinformation that we all learned in school. If you look at the spectrum of light, you will note that it is composed of six bands of light: red, orange, yellow, green, blue, and violet. There is no indigo. It was Isaac Newton's interest in numerology that gave us the color indigo in the ROY G. BIV rainbow that you have all learned. There is really no indigo in the spectrum; since seven was such a mystical and important number, he just felt that there should be seven colors in the spectrum, and so he tossed it in. And ever since then, folks have been taught that there are seven colors in the spectrum, despite the fact that there aren't, and that anyone gazing through a prism or a diffraction grating will find this out.

Of course, if we throw out indigo, we will need a new acronym for the spectrum, something cool enough to replace indigo. If anyone has any ideas, please do pass them on!

In this lab, you will do some experiments on a model of the eye that will allow you to better understand how it is a simple - yet effective - optical device that collects and senses light. At the heart of its workings is a lens that projects an image onto a light-sensing surface. In fact, the optical system of the eye is, essentially, the same as that of a camera!

Let's move on to some theory, and then to some experiments. And no one will be asked to stick anything in their eye.

Necessary Theory

Structure of the Eye

What follows is some of the theory of how your eye works; additional information can be obtained from your text or from the lecture.

Figure 1: The best way to use a magnifying lens is really not like this gentleman is doing. For best effect, you should hold the lens right near your eye. This has the effect of adding the power of the lens to the power of your eye—effectively making you nearsighted! This means that you can bring an object very close to your eye and see it in focus. It appears bigger, but this is just because it is closer. Think of how a jeweler uses a loupe; this is how you should use a magnifying glass. Of course, if you are nearsighted, it's even easier: the point of the magnifying lens is to make you nearsighted—but you already are! If you are nearsighted, just take off your glasses, and you can look at things close up. As I get older and my near point is receding, this is a useful trick that I use more often than I would like to admit!

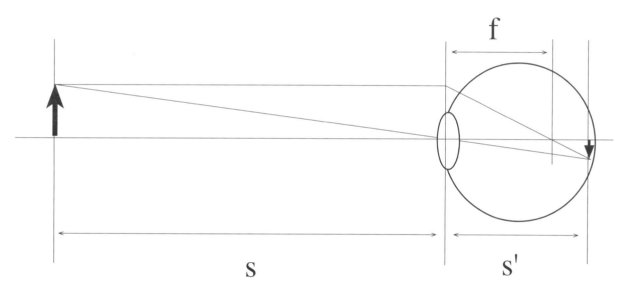

Figure 2: Your eye has a curved front surface, the cornea, that provides most of the focusing power of the eye's optical system. Behind the cornea is the lens, which provides additional focusing power. The important thing about the lens is that it is adjustable: the power of the lens can be varied over a range of several diopters. You use this to focus on near and far objects. As you age, and as the lens loses its ability to accommodate (this is what the change in shape is called) there is a narrower range of things that are in focus. What happens to most people is that they lose their near vision. Their far vision is OK, but their lens can't accommodate enough to make near objects in focus.

We will model the eye as a single focusing element in front of a screen—the retina. The basic optics of your eye are just like you have seen for a thin lens that makes a real image. The lens and the distances (focal length, object, image) are noted. It's a pretty simple optical system, really. In this lab, you will work with a model of the eye that is exactly this: a simple lens that makes an image on a screen.

The basic structure of your eye works like this: a thin lens of focal length f (really the crystalline lens of your eye plus the cornea) projects the image of a source of light, say a candle, on a screen: the retina of your eye. The image is real, of course, and so is inverted. The distances are as in Figure 2: f is the focal length of your eye's lens, s is the distance from the source or object to the lens (to the center of the lens), and s' is the distance from the lens to the image - which is the length of your eye. The following relationship - the same equation as for any thin lens - holds among the distances:

$$\frac{1}{s} + \frac{1}{s'} = \frac{1}{f}$$

The distance from the lens to the retina is fixed - and so to focus on objects at different positions, the eye changes its shape. This has the effect of adjusting f - until you reach an age at which your eye can no longer do this effectively, in which case you get reading glasses!

Given the form of the equation for the distances shown, it is often more convenient to work in terms of the power of a lens instead of the focal length. The power is defined as follows:

power (in diopters) = 1/f (f is in meters)

If you need corrective lenses, the effective power of your eye's lens plus an added lens is just the sum of the powers of your eye's lens (f_1) plus the power of the lens added to it (f_2):

$$\frac{1}{f} = \frac{1}{f_1} + \frac{1}{f_2}$$

The power of the eye's lens should be about 60 diopters; suppose a person's lens has a power of only 57 diopters. This person will be farsighted. But, if they use a corrective lens, in eyeglasses or a contact lens, with a power of 3 diopters, the total power will be 60 diopters—just what it should be.

Vision Defects and Correction

A normal eye will have a focusing system (cornea plus lens) that has a power of about 60 diopters when relaxed. The distance from the lens to the retina is approximately 1.7 cm; let's make it 1.67

cm to make the math work out nicely. So, for a normal eye (s'=1.67 cm) with a relaxed lens (1/f =60) an object will be in focus if it is at a distance of:

$$\frac{1}{s} + \frac{1}{.0167 \text{ m}} = \frac{1}{f} = 60$$

$$\frac{1}{s} + 60 = 60$$

$$\frac{1}{s} = 0$$

$$s = \infty$$

That is, the eye is focused at infinity - on a distant object. So if someone is staring out the window, gazing into the distance, they might just be giving the muscles in their eyes a rest. If your eye is to focus on a near object, muscles in the eye squeeze the lens to make it thicker in the middle. This makes the power greater. Suppose your lens can accommodate down to a power of 64 diopters; this means that the eye can focus on something at a distance of:

$$\frac{1}{s} + \frac{1}{.0167 \text{ m}} = \frac{1}{f} = 64$$

$$\frac{1}{s} + 60 = 64$$

$$\frac{1}{s} = 4$$

$$s = 0.25 \text{ m}$$

The eye will be focused on something at a distance of approximately 25 cm away. If this is the maximum power of the lens of the eye, this is as close as the eye can focus: this distance is what we call the *near point* of the eye.

As you age, your eye will be able to provide less and less accommodation; this is a condition called *presbyopia*. When you get to be well over 40, you will find that your eye can only focus to about 61 diopters; this would mean a near point of 1 meter! You have seen older folks holding things well away from their faces in order to focus on them - this is why. Of course, you can also correct this condition with the addition of a lens. You can get reading glasses, which are slightly converging lenses, to add power to the lens of the eye. If your near point is 1 meter (and the focusing power of your lens is 61 diopters, as above), so you are having to hold the newspaper at arm's length to read it, if you get reading glasses with a power of +3 diopters, you will have a total power of your eye's lens plus the reading glasses of 64 diopters. As we saw, this gives a near point of 25 cm - a perfectly comfortable reading distance.

Of course, some folks need glasses at earlier ages. Suppose the power of the lens in a person's eye is 64 diopters when relaxed, and it accommodates down to 70 diopters. This means that the eye will focus at 25 cm when relaxed, and the near point will be:

$$\frac{1}{s} + 60 = 70$$
$$\frac{1}{s} = 10$$
$$s = 0.10 \text{ m}$$

This is a near point of 10 cm, and a far point of 25 cm. This person is clearly nearsighted; we also call this condition *myopia*. The solution is a diverging lens, with a negative power. Given the above equations, you can see that the appropriate lens would have a power of -4 diopters. This would make the person's far point at infinity, and their near point at 17 cm. They lose some near vision, but now can focus on distant objects, which is a good trade.

Now suppose that the power of a person's lens is 58, and can accommodate down to a power of 62. Any power less than 60 is useless; if the lens is down to a power of 60, the eye is focused at infinity - there is no need to relax the lens any further. This person will have good distance vision, but won't be able to see as well as they could at short distances: they are farsighted. The condition is also known as *hyperopia*. The solution is, of course, a converging lens. What power lens should the person of this example use?

In all of the preceding calculations, we have assumed a certain value for s' - the length of the eye. This is just for purposes of illustration. In practice, an optometrist will measure how much correction a person's vision needs by trying different lenses to see which one gives the best results.

Experiments and Calculations

Equipment Needed

Each lab group will receive:
Eye model
Light source with arrow, grid
Cardboard with star-shaped cutout
Pinhole viewer (film cannister with single pinhole in lid, trio in bottom)
Corrective lenses: converging, diverging
Astigmatic lenses
Magnifiers with two lenses - enough for everyone in your group

The eye models are pretty pricey and pretty cool, so we will ask you to use care with them - we would like for them to last for many years. These eyes focus by changing the shape of the lens of the eye not as your eye does - by using muscles to compress the lens and change its shape - but by using a syringe to pump more or less water into the lens, causing it to bulge or flatten. Please don't overfill the lens; if you find that there is a fair amount of resistance to your adding more water to the lens by depressing the syringe, that's probably because you are trying to fill it too full.

Of course, you can use the eye model to focus and make an image of anything, but you might want to start with the source that we have provided. This source has an arrow on one side, so that you can check to see if the projected image is inverted or not, and it also has a grid that you can use to test for astigmatism, as we will see later.

First Steps: Getting an Image on the Retina

Turn on your light source, and position it some distance away from your eye model. Check to see that the "retina" of the model - the screen that images will be projected on - is set at the middle position. Now adjust the amount of water in the lens to change its shape; you should be able to bring the object into focus.

QUESTION

What do you notice about the orientation of the image? How does your brain correct for this?

The image on your retina is, in fact, upside down. If you project something on your retina that is right side up, your brain will happily invert it for you...

EXPERIMENT

Use one of the pinhole viewers (the film cannister with a single pinhole in the lid and three pinholes in a triangle arrangement in the bottom) as follows: look through the pinhole in the lid at the three pinholes in the bottom, and adjust them so that the form an upright triangle. Note the orientation of the arrangement of pinholes carefully. Next, being careful to keep the orientation of the triangle fixed, turn the cannister so that the side with the three pinholes is very close to your eye. What do you notice about the orientation of the triangle now?

What is happening is this: the triangle of pinholes is illuminated by the light from the pinhole in the lid. All of this is so close to your eye that there is no way for your eye to focus. In fact, what will happen is that a shadow will be projected on your retina. But the shadow will not be inverted; it will appear right side up!

QUESTION

Why does this mean that the image appears as it does? Explain what is happening?

The eye models that we have do not have an iris - an aperture that can be used to increase or decrease the amount of light that enters the eye. But we can add one - and we will. But we will add one that has an unusual shape....

EXPERIMENT

Place the piece of cardboard with the star-shaped cutout in front of the lens of your eye model. How does this affect the image that you see?

In fact, you should see that the cutout only serves to dim the image - not change its shape. This "iris" appears in front of the lens, before the light is brought to a focus. Therefore it will only block light from the lens - not any particular piece of the image. When your iris closes down, when you come into a region with bright light, you don't see this - you do not perceive a change in the edge of your field of view!

Accommodation

Next, we will look at changing the shape of the lens in order to bring objects at different distances into focus.

EXPERIMENT

Move your object closer to your eye model. How must you adjust the shape of the lens so that the image is in focus again? What do you notice about the size of the image, compared to the previous case? As you change the shape of the lens, do you make it more or less converging? What does this do to the power of the lens, in diopters?

EXPERIMENT

Move your object so that it is farther from your eye model than it was originally. How must you adjust the shape of the lens so that the image is in focus again? What do you notice about the size of the image, compared to the previous case? As you change the shape of the lens, do you make it more or less converging? What does this do to the power of the lens, in diopters?

This process of changing the shape of the lens to adjust its power to bring objects at differing distances into focus is known as accommodation. Of course, as there is a limit to how far the lens can be distorted, there is a limit to how far the lens can accommodate - and to how close the eye can focus.

QUESTION

What is the near point of your eye model?

Figure 3: Test for the position of your blind spot and for astigmatism

Blind Spot

If your strongest eye is your left eye:

Close your right eye, hold the paper about 30 cm (12 inches) away from your face, and focus on the dot. Move the paper back and forth, slowly; at some point, the star should disappear.

If your strongest eye is your right eye:

Close your left eye, hold the paper about 30 cm (12 inches) away from your face, and focus on the star. Move the paper back and forth, slowly; at some point, the dot should disappear.

Astigmatism Test

Do some of the lines in the diagram below seem a bit lighter or less distinct than the others?

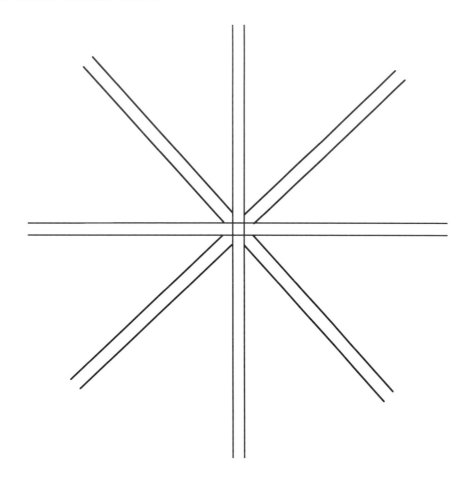

Note: in fact, you can adjust the lens to focus about as close as you want. Your instructor will give you a range of values for the syringe that you can work in. At the furthest allowed press of the syringe, when the lens is at its fattest, how close can you move the object and still keep the image of it in focus?

EXPERIMENT

What is the far point of your eye model? That is, how far away can you move the object and still keep the image in focus? (Note: you may not be able to reach the far point; if it is at infinity, you won't be able to put the object any farther away than this! If you can't get to the far point, call it "infinity."

EXPERIMENT

Next, move the object closer to the eye model than this near point. You should now see that you are not able to get the image into focus.

EXPERIMENT

Now, add a converging lens to the stand in front of your eye. Are you able to get the image into focus now? What is the new near point? As you move the object closer to the eye model - as you are able to do now - what happens to the size of the image that you observe?

This is essentially what a magnifying lens does for you: it allows you to focus on objects that are closer to your eye, so that the image will appear larger on your retina. This is a very simple form of optical aid.

QUESTION

As a person ages, his or her lens loses ability to accommodate - the muscles in the eye can relax and the lens will be focused on a distant object, but as the lens stiffens with age and the muscles weaken, the eye will be less able to vary the power of the lens. How would this affect your near point? This condition is called *presbyopia,* and everyone gets it sooner or later. What sort of lens could you use to correct for this particular vision problem?

Vision Correction

Everyone develops presbyopia sooner or later, but some people develop vision defects long before this becomes an issue. There are two main types of vision defect:

• Hyperopia, or farsightedness. In this case, the lens of the eye is not strongly focusing enough, and an image would form behind the retina.

• Myopia, or nearsightedness. In this case, the lens of the eye is too strongly focusing, and an image forms in front of the retina.

In order to simulate these two vision defects, we will change the position of the "retina" in the eye model: you can put it farther back from the lens to produce an eye that is nearsighted, and you can put it closer to the lens to produce an eye that is farsighted.

EXPERIMENT

Adjust the position of the "retina" in your eye model so that it is farther back; this will make a nearsighted eye. What are the near and far points for the eye as it is?

QUESTION

How would you correct for this particular vision defect? Would you add a converging lens or a diverging lens?

EXPERIMENT

Add what you feel is the appropriate lens, and then test: what are the near and far points now? Are these close to what you measured before for the "normal" eye?

Next, let's look at the other end of the spectrum of things:

EXPERIMENT

Adjust the position of the "retina" in your eye model so that it is closer to the lens; this will make a farsighted eye. What are the near and far points for the eye as it is?

EXPERIMENT

How would you correct for this particular vision defect? (Is this a defect? The eye can still focus on distant objects. What limits does this eye have?) Would you add a converging lens or a diverging lens to correct this condition?

EXPERIMENT

Add what you feel is the appropriate lens, and then test: what are the near and far points now? Are these close to what you measured before for the "normal" eye?

Astigmatism

Another kind of common vision defect is astigmatism: this means that the lens does not have a single focal point, but will focus at different points depending on the orientation of an image. In order to get an idea of where this comes from - and what can be done about it - we will add a lens to your eye model that will have the effect of making the eye astigmatic.

EXPERIMENT

Add a cylindrical lens to your eye model. Since the lens has a cylindrical shape, it will focus light along either the horizontal or the vertical axis - but it will have no effect on the other axis. (Note: the cylindrical lens that you will use has a definite axis to it; it will be important to have it oriented correctly. There will be some sort of mark on the lens to show you how it should be oriented.) Set your eye model back for a normal position for the "retina." Now, focus your eye model on the grid portion of your light source. Focus on the vertical lines in the grid; what do you notice about

the horizontal lines? Next, focus on the horizontal lines; what do you notice about the vertical lines? When you are focused at one or the other spot, try rotating the lens. This should move the different sets of lines in and out of focus.

In order to produce an astigmatism, we added a cylindrical lens. In order to correct for an astigmatism, you would have eyeglasses with cylindrical lenses. In fact, if you look at a prescription, it will list a "sphere" and a "cylinder" number, along with an angle. You can make a single lens that has both spherical and cylindrical components that will correct for both nearsightedness or farsightedness and an astigmatism at the same time.

QUESTION

Figure 3 has a grid that can be used for a quick test for astigmatism. Explain, briefly, how it works.

Fun with Floaters

We saw earlier how that an object that was very close to your eye was too close for you to focus on it - and so you could cast a shadow of it on your retina. In fact, you can do something like this with distant objects with interesting results - if you adjust your vision accordingly.

This experiment can be done by everyone in your group at the same time - you should have enough magnifiers for everyone. Make this a fun and exciting group experience.

EXPERIMENT

Take one of the magnifiers that you have been given, pick one eye to work with, and hold the smaller of the two lenses right up near your eye. Look at a distant, small light source (perhaps the light source at another lab table?) and note its appearance.

In fact, when you see a circle of light rather than a sharp image, what you are seeing is the shadow of your iris. Now try this:

EXPERIMENT

As you look at the light through one eye, open and close your other eye, and watch the change in the circle of light. You should see it change; what is causing this change?

EXPERIMENT

Note that your eyes work together to determine the size of your pupils: even if one eye is closed and the other open, the size of the two pupils should be the same! If you close one eye, it will be receiving very little light, and so both of your pupils should get larger. When you open this eye, both pupils should contract. What does this do to the image that you see?

(Note: both of your pupils should - and under most circumstances, do - work together. This is one thing that a medical practictioner will check for if you have had a blow to the head. If you ever bonked your head and got taken to the emergency room as a child, you will no doubt have fond memories of a doctor shining a flashlight in your eye. What the doctor was doing was shining light on one eye and seeing if the pupil in the other eye changed size - if it did, then things were hunky dory. If it didn't, well, that meant that you needed a bit more attention.)

EXPERIMENT

Since the distant point light source casts a shadow on your retina, it will cast a shadow of stuff in your eye on your retina. Use the small lens in front of one eye again and look at a distant point light source. You will see, as before, a circle of light. Now look at the circle of light more carefully. Some of the things you might notice:

• Look at the edges of the circle of light. The edge is not smooth; this is because the tissues that define the edge of your pupil are not smooth - and you are seeing a shadow of this edge.

• You will likely see some "floaters" in the circle of light. These are bits of goo on the surface of your eye or in your eye. Blink your eye and see how the floaters move. Question: why do the floaters seem to move up after you blink your eye? What way are they really moving?

• Close your eyelids slowly. You should be able to see a shadow of your eyelid coming across your pupil, plus the shadow of your eyelashes.

• Finally, note the shape of the circle of light that you see. If it is more of an oval than a circle, this means that you have an astigmatism. Why?

Summing Up

If you wear glasses or contact lenses, you are most likely nearsighted. Over the years, as I poll my classes, I find that about 90% of folks who wear glasses are nearsighted - farsighted folks are definitely in the minority. It would seem that vision defects should be more symmetrical - that about half of folks would be nearsighted and about half would be farsighted. Unless there is somethings that tends to make folks nearsighted...

And there may well be. When I was a kid, and I would make a face, adults would say, "someday your face will just stay that way." But when I would sit and read, no one would say to me, "if you keep compressing the lenses in your eyes to focus close, someday they will just stay that way." And, of course, at some point, they did. Folks who do a lot of close work keep the lenses in their eyes compressed quite a bit of the time, and, at some point, they might stay compressed - and so make the lens have too much power even when relaxed. These folks might end up being nearsighted. There are other factors at work, but this might well be an issue.

If you are nearsighted, take heart, though. Here is a little experiment that someone who is nearsighted can do any time they would like - and it only works for nearsighted folks. If you are nearsighted, try this sometime: take off your glasses, and look at a distant light source. It should look like a circle of light. What you are seeing, as before, is a shadow - of your pupil. You can repeat all of the experiments that we did before - plus at least one more. If you look at a distant source of light through a screen (perhaps you are standing on the porch, looking through the screen door wistfully at some distant light source, for some reason known only to you; perhaps you are even brushing a small bitter tear from your cheek...) you can see a shadow of the screen as well.

I used to amuse myself this way when I was a kid. In Columbus, Ohio, where I grew up, we had a minor league baseball team called the Columbus Jets. My brothers and I had Junior Jet badges that meant that we could get into all of the baseball games for a whole summer for just one dollar. My folks got season tickets, and that meant that we could go to about as many baseball games as we wanted to. And given that my father was a major sports fan, and that whatever he wanted turned into what we all wanted, we wanted to go to a lot of baseball games.

And so we did. But I found the pace of the game a bit slow at times, and so I looked for other ways to amuse myself. One of the ways that I did this was to look at the lights that lit up the field during night games. Since I was nearsighted, they appeared as nice circles, and I could make them change size and such at my whim. This sort of entertainment could keep me going at least until the seventh inning stretch.

Go in peace.

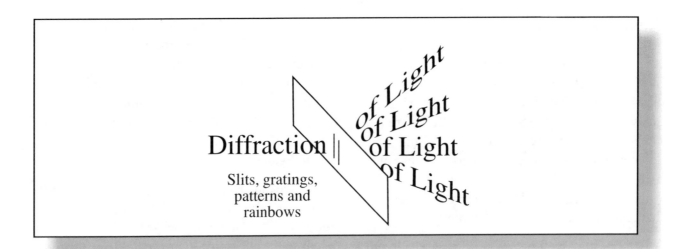

Diffraction

Slits, gratings,
patterns and
rainbows

of Light
of Light
of Light
of Light

Opening Remarks

By this time in the year, you are possibly wearying of physics. Perhaps you even feel as strongly as a politician of the last century:

"I am tired of this thing called science.... We have spent millions on that sort of thing for the last few years, and it is time it should be stopped."

- Simon Cameron, U.S. Senator from Pennsylvania, demanding that the funding of the Smithsonian Institution be cut off, 1861.

It is rare to find a politician with such candor. Fortunately, science and the Smithsonian Institution have continued. The Smithsonian has an interesting history: it was founded by a man named Smithson, who was the illegitimate son of a very wealthy Englishman. Due to his birth circumstances, he was never accepted by polite society in England, and he left his fortune to the budding young United States, which he felt was less conscious of such distinctions.

Science also has this strength of looking less at surface appearances. It is an approach that looks for fundamental truths, beyond what people believe.

One of the great debates in science that raged for many years was the nature of light. Is it a particle or a wave? There are arguments for both sides; the clearest signal that light has a wavelike nature is given by diffraction. Diffraction occurs when light passes obstacles or slits that are not so large compared to its wavelength. Ordinary objects like tables and chairs do not qualify, but a thin slit does: light that passes though such a thin slit shows a clear pattern of diffraction and interference.

In this lab, we will be looking at the patterns resulting from light passing through single, double, and multiple slits. It is an interesting, visual lab, with definite practical applications.

Necessary Theory

To begin, we recall the basic principles of producing a diffraction pattern. Consider a collimated beam of light incident on a slit. We can use Huygens' principle to look at this situation. Before the slit we have plane waves; the situation after the slit is more complicated. Each point in the slit is viewed as being a source of spherical "wavelets." The distortion of the wave in passing through the slit is called diffraction. The wavelets from the different points in the slit can interfere with each other; in this lab we will be looking at the resulting interference pattern.

The Single Slit

For light incident on a single slit, the resulting interference pattern will consist of a series of alternating light and dark bands. The key feature is that the width of the central bright band is twice the width of the other bright bands.

Figure 1: Fluffy and Spot would sit around for hours debating such philosophical issues as the wave-particle duality of light, the existence and species of God, why cats don't come when they are called, and why dogs like to sniff people in embarrassing places.

Figure 2: Congratulations on what is likely your final formal physics lab in the first year physics sequence. We hope that you have increased in your understanding of the physical world, and that your experience will save you from embarrassing social gaffes such as the one illustrated above.

A question: how does the pattern change if the width of the slit is varied?

The Double Slit

If instead of a single slit the beam of light is incident on a double slit we also obtain an interference pattern. If the slits are very narrow compared to their separation, the slits can be considered as point sources of spherical waves; these spherical waves will interfere and produce a pattern of light and dark bands. In this case, the light bands will be of identical widths.

Some questions: how does the pattern change if the width of the slits is changed? How is the pattern affected if the separation of the slits is changed?

Multiple Slits and Gratings

If we continue adding slits, assuming the separation does not change, the basic pattern does not change, but the "bands" discussed above become more well-defined. Eventually, in the case of many slits (a grating), the orders will be very well-defined points, at well-specified angles. Such a grating is useful in measuring the spectrum of light, as the angle of a given order depends on the wavelength according to the following equation:

$$d \sin\theta = m\lambda$$

d is the grating spacing, θ the angle of the order, m the order number, and λ the wavelength of light. As you can see, light of many wavelengths can be broken up into a spectrum by a grating. This is a powerful experimental technique.

Experiments and Calculations

Necessary Equipment

There will be four sets of equipment for viewing patterns from different sets of slits. Please note that the lasers that we use pose no real danger to your vision, but good laser hygeine demands that you keep the beam and direct reflections out of your eyes.

Laser and supports

Cornell diffraction plate in stand
Magnifying glass
Screen
Holder for hair (in stand)
Meter stick

Do not use chalk dust in these areas to make the laser beams visible!!! This makes a great mess and will damage the equipment.

In addition, each table will have equipment for measuring the spectral lines of gases:

Gas tube in stand, with supply
Grating in stand
Meter sticks

This is equipment to make a sort of DIY (do-it-yourself) spectrometer.

There are two parts to this experiment: looking at diffraction patterns from the slits on the Cornell plate, and making measurements of gas spectra. You should start with one experiment or the other; there is no particular intended order.

The Cornell Plate

This portion of the experiment is intended to be a reasonably open-ended investigation. Use the Cornell plate in the setup as shown in Figure 4 to look at the diffraction pattern from different parts of the plate, corresponding to different sets of slits. Use the magnifying glass to deduce what each of the columns on the plate correspond to. The sets of slits are grouped in a natural fashion; see Figure 3. One column corresponds to increasing numbers of slits of the same separation. Other columns have similar themes; once you figure out what the columns are, you can use this to guide your investigations.

As always, you should follow the scientific method: make a prediction, test, and analyze.

Get a pattern from a single slit on the screen.

PREDICTION

How is the pattern affected by increasing the width of the slit?

Test your prediction.

156

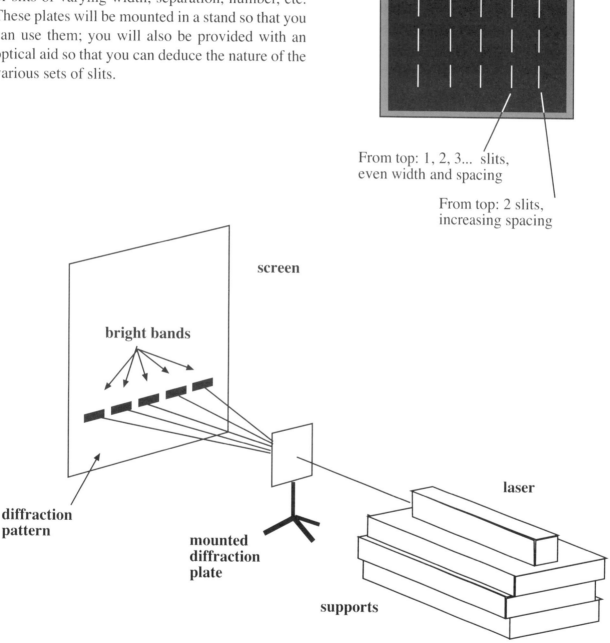

Figure 3: The Cornell diffraction plate has columns of slits of varying width, separation, number, etc. These plates will be mounted in a stand so that you can use them; you will also be provided with an optical aid so that you can deduce the nature of the various sets of slits.

From top: 1, 2, 3... slits, even width and spacing

From top: 2 slits, increasing spacing

screen

bright bands

diffraction pattern

laser

mounted diffraction plate

supports

Figure 4: The diffraction plate is mounted as shown, and a laser is pointed at one part of the plate. In the example shown, the laser illuminates a pair of slits; the pattern shown appears on the screen behind the plate. Placing the screen well back and performing the experiment in a darkened room help make the pattern more visible.

Next, get a pattern from a double slit on the screen. Can you see the single slit pattern too? The double slit pattern is the interference between two of these single slit patterns, so there will be lighter and darker portions of the pattern.

PREDICTION

How will the pattern be affected by increasing the separation between the slits? Note: there is one column on the Cornell plate that has double slits with continuously varying separation. By adjusting your jack stand, you can continuously vary the pattern. Make a prediction as to what you will see.

Do you find what you predicted?

Next we consider multiple slit patterns; there is a column on the Cornell plate that has multiple slits: 2, 5, etc. in increasing numbers.

PREDICTION

How should a multiple-slit pattern be affected by increasing the number of slits? Make a prediction, and test.

Beyond this, you can make observations guided by what you find on the plate; experiment as you see fit. Record your observations; be quantitative if you see a natural way to do so. Note: you can make marks on the (paper) screen to facilitate comparisons of different patterns if you are sure to replace the screen when you finish.

Width of a Hair

Consider the diffraction pattern from a single slit: the light passes through an obstruction like:

Clearly, this is just the inverse of:

(Recall the situation of the pinhole and the anti-pinhole you may have seen previously.) Thus, we expect to see a diffraction pattern from a thin obstruction that is the *inverse* of the pattern from the single slit. An obvious choice for the obstruction is a hair; a hair held in a beam of laser will produce a diffraction pattern. The interesting thing about this is that a measurement of the spacing of the pattern of light and dark bands should allow you to deduce the thickness of the hair producing this pattern. Some cautions:

• The pattern is not that easy to see.

• Persons with curly hair, such as myself, have hair that has an elliptical cross section. This means that the measured width will depend on the orientation. It is better to pick a group member with straight hair.

Once you have plucked a hair from one of your group, use the holder provided to use the hair to obstruct the beam.

PUZZLE

What measurements must you take to determine the thickness of a hair? Can you come up with a basic working equation that will allow you to quickly determine a hair thickness from one measurement? Those with programmable calculators (you could also use the computers) should try to make a routine that, when one number is entered, a hair thickness will be calculated. Test your technique on the measurement of a hair from one of your group members. Does the number seem reasonable?

You can, if you wish, borrow a micrometer to check your results. Which is more accurate: the diffraction technique, or the micrometer?

Try hair from different group members. Do you see differences in different hair types? Can you tell, for curly hair, that the cross section is in fact elliptical?

Line Spectra of Gases

As noted in the Theory section, a diffraction grat-

158

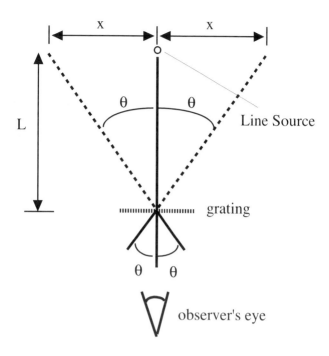

Figure 5: The system we will utilize for viewing the spectral lines of the different sources has the geometry above. You look through the grating as shown; the spectral lines are perceived to come from an angle that can be deduced from a measurement of x and L.

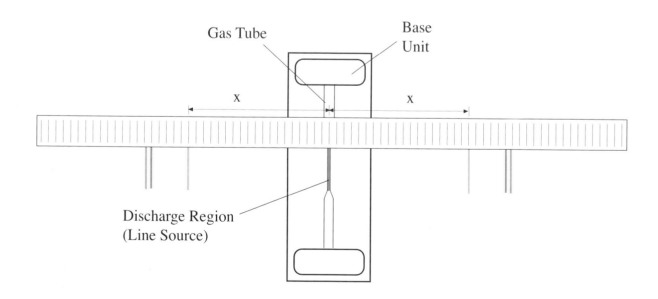

Figure 6: A front view of the situation in Figure 5. The observer views the spectral lines as shown. By a measurement of the distance x, the wavelength of a particular line can be deduced.

ing produces a sharp pattern with orders appearing at specific angles depending on the wavelength of light. This is a powerful analytical tool that lets us measure the spectrum of light.

In this lab you will have the chance to measure the spectrum of gases in discharge tubes. These tubes are very thin in the region of the discharge; viewing the tube through a diffraction grating will produce a set of images of the tube at different spacings corresponding to the different wavelengths present. There will be several different types of tubes available, with different types of gases. A quick look through the grating will show the spectrum; a comparison with the wall chart should enable you to deduce what gas is in the tube. The grating that you will look through is mounted in a holder on the edge of the table. You will be handling it during the lab; be careful to always hold it by the edge of the holder - **never touch the glass**!

In addition to an overall view of the different spectral lines produced by the source, you can do reasonably accurate quantitative measurements of the wavelengths of the lines in a spectrum by using a meter stick scale. Recall that the larger the wavelength of light the greater the angle that it will be diffracted by. A meter stick scale can be used to measure this angle in an indirect fashion. Suppose you stand in front of the line source (the thin spectrum tube) and look at it through the grating; a meter stick is set just in front of the tube as shown in Figure 6. Looking straight ahead you see the slit with light emerging from it. But if you look to either side you will see a first order spectrum. Your eye traces the rays backwards as shown in Figure 5; you perceive the fringes to be very distant (the rays that form the image are parallel). If you try, you can visually superimpose them on the scale that sticks out each side of the collimated source. This will enable you to measure x and λ; you will then be able to compute θ.

PUZZLE

Write down a basic working equation for your setup that will let you determine a wavelength from a measured value of x. What other measurements do you need?

Turn on the power supply to a tube and let it warm up. Position the grating at the end of the table on which the source is resting; the source should be in the middle, with a meter stick supported just in front. Now look through the grating at the source. You should see the scale and the source; you should also see, to the right and the left of the source, images of the first order spectrum of the gas in the tube. The spectrum should appear well out toward the end of the scale. If you look carefully you should also be able to see the second order spectrum, and perhaps even a few lines of higher order spectra. We will not be using them for calculations.

To make quantitative measurements, make sure that the grating is parallel to the scale and as closely as possible adjust it so that it is along the line directly from the slit. While one person looks through the grating, have another person move a pencil point or some other marker so that it shows the position of one line on either side of the source. The distance from the center will be the value of x. A measurement of x should be the same on both sides. Is it? If not, make adjustments so that it is. What will you have to adjust?

Once the apparatus is fully adjusted, take your measurements. First make a careful measurement of L. Should L be measured to the meter stick or to the tube? Think about it. Next, measure the values of x for some of the more prominent lines. Using measured values of L and x, calculate the values of θ and then the values of λ for each line (using the equation in the Theory section, and the grating spacing noted on the grating holder). Your instructor will have a table of the known wavelengths for some of the sources you will be using; compare the values that you obtain with these. You should get reasonable agreement.

You may also wish to look at the spectrum of other sources in the room: sunlight coming in the window, fluorescent tubes in the ceiling, light from the computer screen, etc. The fluorescent tubes in the ceiling are mercury vapor tubes; can you tell this from their spectrum?

160

Summary

This is the last page of what will likely be the last formal lab of the semester; if you are still reading all of the text at this point, I commend you. We hope that the lab has been of some assistance to you in mastering physics; we also hope that you will have positive memories of the course and the lab. If you have enjoyed the lab half as much as I have enjoyed putting it together, then I have enjoyed it twice as much as you.

We in the Physics Department wish you all the best for your future study, and we leave you with these sound words of advice from Lewis Carroll:

"Speak in French when you can't think of the English for a thing, turn out your toes when you walk, and remember who you are!"

- *Through the Looking Glass, ch. 2*

Go in peace.

The Nature of Light

Fun With Light-Emitting Diodes

Opening Remarks

Student: "So what's the truth? Is light a particle or a wave?"

Instructor: "Yes."

This is a real exchange that took place in a class that I taught. Needless to say, the student was less than satisfied with my answer.

This sort of thing happens from time to time; see Figure 1 for more details. But the fact is, my answer was literally true—light is a particle or a wave. Think back to the diffraction of light lab. In order to understand what is going on in this lab, it is crucial that you think of light as a wave. In fact, you calculated wavelengths for the light! But in today's lab, you will do a measurement that suggests quite strongly that light must be considered as a particle—it seems to come in chunks of a particular size.

But here is the cool thing: exactly what light appears to be depends on what you are doing. If you are looking for wave properties, you will find waves; if you are looking for particle properties, you will find particles. Light *is* a particle or a wave.

We won't get too much in depth into this puzzle. Instead, we will finesse it. Let's just say that light is made up of photons, which are packets of energy. They are quantized; each photon will have an energy that corresponds to its frequency. And these

photons have wavelengths, too, calculated from the frequency. So, photons are like particles with a wave nature. And that is what light is: photons.

Now, let's get down to business: just how are we going to show that light is made of photons?

Necessary Theory

Quantization

Around the turn of the century, there were a number of problems that physicists were working on that showed shortcomings in the physics of the time. One vexing problem was blackbody radiation—the kind of radiation that is emitted by a simple incandescent bulb, and other sources of light that glow simply because they are hot. Classical theories predicted that the amount of energy emitted should grow without bound as frequency increased—so that a light bulb would give off vast amounts of ultraviolet light, and, even worse, an infinite amount of energy. Clearly, this had to be untrue, and the problem was known as the "ultraviolet catastrophe."

Max Planck found a way around this by invoking quantization (actually his formula started out as an empirical formula to fit the data, but it worked so well he worked hard to justify it.) He assumed that energy could not come in any particular amount, but that it had to come in "chunks" of value hf, where h

162

Figure 1: The above exchange really did happen in a graduate E&M class at Colorado State. (Etters et. al., note on graduate student office door with confirming verbal communication.)

is a constant we now know as Planck's constant and f the frequency. At higher frequencies, the energy had to come in larger and larger chunks—and at some point, the amount of energy emitted would drop off with frequency due to this.

But here is a conceptual problem: what are the "chunks?" We now know them as photons; electromagnetic radiation is given off in quantized units called photons. Photons have an energy given by:

$$E = hf$$

where h is Planck's constant.

Photoelectric Effect

There was another experimental problem at the time that this photon picture was nicely able to handle: the photoelectric effect. The effect is this: when light strikes a metal surface, it may eject electrons from it. Philip Lenard had shown in 1902 that the energy of electrons emitted from such a metal surface was independent of the intensity of the incident light—which is very hard to explain in the classical theory. More light means more energy, and more energy should mean more ener-

getic electrons—but it doesn't. More light means more electrons, but the energy per electron doesn't change.

Does this sound like quantization again? It did to Einstein. He explained this effect by generalizing from Planck's hypothesis, assuming essentially this: light is made up of photons, each of which has some energy. Each photon can knock one electron off a metal surface; the energy that the electron ends up with will be the energy of the photon minus the work function—a measure of the energy necessary to free the electron. More photons means more electrons freed, but the energy of the electrons thus freed will be the same.

Einstein went further to predict a specific relationship between the energy of the electrons and the energy of the photons that was subsequently tested by Millikan and found to be valid. Einstein won the Nobel Prize for the theory, and Millikan for the experiment and his eponymous oil-drop experiment. It is interesting to note that Einstein did not win the Nobel for what he is most known for: relativity.

In this lab, we will do an experiment that allows us to compare the energy of electrons (which we can measure directly) to the energy of photons (which we can deduce using equation (1) above.) It will not be as direct at the standard photoelectric effect experiment (if you want to do this, please take PH 315, our Modern Physics lab) but it will allow us to make a definite comparison. You should see that the photon picture of light explains your observations quite well.

The lab will be based on light-emitting diodes. In the next section, we will discuss a little bit about these LEDs to give you enough background in order to understand the experiment.

Light-Emitting Diodes: The Simple Picture

I am not going to give you a total band-structure picture of how LEDs work; to be honest, this would raise more questions than it would answer. Let's look at LEDs as black boxes, not worrying about their internal structure. This seems like a cop-out, but it isn't really; looking at these devices externally will pretty much tell us what we need to know about them.

A basic LED circuit is shown in Figure 2. The power supply drives a current through the LED, and it gives off light. We assume that the power supply has a voltage of 2.0 V; this is a reasonably typical value for LEDs. Electron current is shown in the diagram too.

Now look at Figure 3. This shows the energy of the electron at different places in the circuit, and how the energy of the electron changes as it moves around. As the electron moves through the power supply, it gains energy:

$$\Delta E_{power\ supply} = +(electron\ charge)(supply\ voltage)$$

$$\Delta E_{power\ supply} = e \cdot 2\ V\ (in\ joules)$$
$$\Delta E_{power\ supply} = 2\ eV\ (electron\text{-}volts)$$

There are two different ways to express the energy—in joules, or electron-volts, which can be more convenient at times.

Now, as the electron moves through the diode, it loses energy. Given that energy is conserved, it must change its energy as follows:

$$\Delta E_{LED} = -\Delta E_{power\ supply}$$
$$\Delta E_{LED} = -e \cdot 2\ V\ (in\ joules)$$
$$\Delta E_{LED} = -2\ eV\ (in\ electron\text{-}volts)$$

Where does this energy go? Some of it will go to heat and other loss mechanisms, but the bulk of it will go to light.

Dare we say that the energy of an electron goes into a single photon? Dare we further suggest that we could calculate the energy of that photon and compare it to the energy of the electron? And do we have the bald-faced audacity to intimate—nay, to suggest—perhaps even to *state*—that the two energies might in fact be commensurate?

We do, and we shall. This is just what you will test in the next section; it will be your quest, as it were.

Experiments and Observations

Necessary Equipment

There are two key pieces to the experimental apparatus that you will use this week:

Electronics bit:

> Power supply
> LED box
> Voltmeter

The power supply is current-limited, so it can't put out enough current to damage the LEDs. Just to be on the safe side, though, when you hook up the LED box turn the voltage down, make the connection, and then turn it back up again. Note that the four LEDs in the boxes have a common ground, which is on the side. The positive terminals for the LEDs are next to the LEDs themselves.

Optics bit:

> Diffraction grating in stand
> Meter stick in stand

This is the same setup that was used last week to measure wavelengths in the Diffraction of Light lab. You may have to change your technique a bit, as the LEDs aren't that bright. Getting good

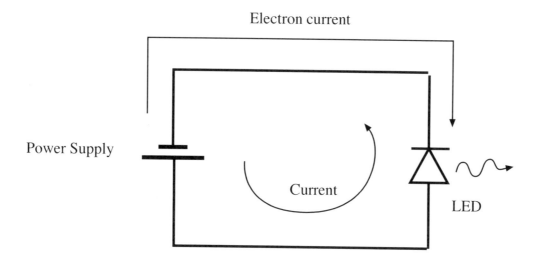

Figure 2: A power supply sends current to an LED, which emits light. The flows of conventional current (which is opposite to the direction of what is actually flowing, electrons) and electron current

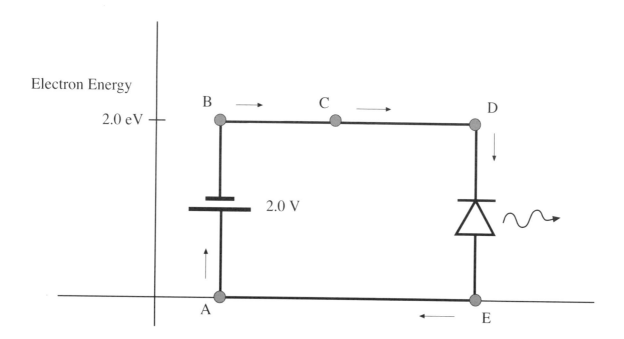

Figure 3: As the electron moves from point A to point B, it gains an energy of 2.0 eV. It keeps this energy as it moves from B to C and C to D, then loses it as it goes from D to E. Where does the energy

measurements will be a bit of a challenge—but heck, you folks are up to it!

Your Quest

Don't forget what this lab is about: you are going to compare the energies of electrons (measured electrically) to the energies of photons these electrons cause to be emitted (by measuring wavelengths), and see if they match. There are two steps here: measuring the energies of electrons and measuring the energies of photons. And there are decisions to be made at each step. The next sections are a rough guide as to how to proceed, but are not cookbook directions. As you read them, remember your quest - your aim in this experiment.

Electrical Measurements

Connect up the red LED to your power supply, attach the voltmeter to measure the voltage across it. You will want to measure the voltage across the LED as it runs.

There's a key question, though, which you need to ask before you continue. When you turn up the voltage, the LED will turn on (very dimly) at some voltage—lets call this the "turn-on voltage," shall we? Of course, it's too darn dim to see at this point, so when you take the spectrum you will want to crank up the voltage a bit. When you get the LED nice and bright, the voltage across it will be higher. Let's call this voltage the "operating voltage," what say?

QUESTION

OK, here's the question: in your analysis, do you want to use the turn-on voltage or the operating voltage? At the turn-on voltage, the energy of the electrons is sufficient to make photons, so you might well want to use this voltage. Using the higher voltage might be an overestimate. On the other hand, when you measure the spectrum you are really looking at photons given off when electrons were given an energy in electron volts equivalent to the operating voltage. So which do you use?

It might be prudent to measure both voltages at this point. One way to proceed would be to try them both and see which works better!

Once you have given this some thought, turn up the voltage and measure the turn-on voltage and the operating voltage of the red LED.

PREDICTION

After doing the red LED, you will want to measure the relevant voltages for the yellow, green and blue LEDs. Before doing so, predict: how will the voltages for these LEDs vary? Predict what the relative values of turn-on and operating voltages will be for the red, yellow, green and blue LEDs. Which will have the highest? The lowest? Why do you predict this?

After you have made a prediction, test: measure voltage values for the other LEDs and compare.

Light Measurements

OK, now it's time to measure the energies of the photons coming off the LEDs. OK, suppose you believe in photons, and that their energies depend on frequency as in Equation (1). Of course, what you will measure is wavelength...

DERIVATION

Derive an equation that gives the energy of a photon in terms of its wavelength.

After you have done this, it's time to measure wavelengths! Fire up the red LED, and use the technique you developed in the Diffraction of Light lab to measure the wavelength it emits.

As you gaze through the diffraction grating, though, you will note: inasmuch as there is ointment, there is a fly in it....

QUESTION

You will note that the LED actually gives off a range of wavelengths—not a single one. So here's the question: which wavelength do you want to use—the middle of the spectrum or one of the ends? Maybe the brightest spot?

OK, here's a hint: suppose an electron comes in with 2 eV of energy. Is it possible (thinking about what you know about energy) for the electron to produce a photon with 2 eV of energy? (Answer: Yessiree, Bob! It just gives all its energy to the photon.) Now, it is possible for the electron to produce a photon with *more* than 2 eV of energy? *Less* than 2 eV of energy? Can you see why there might be a spectrum of energies of photons? Given this, what should you use as the measured wavelength of the light? Think about it, and discuss it in your group. (Note: we don't expect you to make arguments based on knowledge of semiconductors, which we don't expect you to have. We expect you to make arguments based on your knowledge of light and energy—which we do expect you to have.)

Once you have decided what wavelength to use, measure wavelengths for all of the LEDs.

Putting it All Together

Now it's time to work with energies. Make a table in which you list the energy of the electrons in each LED and the energy of the emitted photons for each LED. Do your values agree? Do the energies have a trend that seems sensible? What sources of error are there in this experiment? (Here's something to note about the LEDs too: I think that the red, yellow and green LEDs are pretty similar in how they are constructed. But they have colored cases which change the output spectrum. This is one source of error that you can't get around in this experiment.)

You might want to go back and try different approaches: if you used the turn-on voltage before, use the operating voltage. Maybe you could revisit the question of what you called the wavelength for each LED.

Summing Up

The opening quote was of an exchange in class that left the student who asked the question feeling unsatisfied. The dissatisfaction was not with my flippant response, though, but really with the grayness of the answer: light *is* a particle or a wave. It is this indeterminate, fuzzy aspect of modern physics that upsets people.

The world is a stranger place than you might have imagined. In fact, as someone I can't recall once said, it is a stranger place that you *can* imagine. It is composed of entities that sometimes behave like waves and sometimes like particles. They are identical at a fundamental level—truly indistinguishable. (If you have seen one electron, you have seen them all.) And the basic processes by which they interact are random—truly random, and impossible to predict, no matter what.

If you find all this upsetting, you are in good company. Einstein felt the same way. It is ironic, as he was one of the founding parents of quantum mechanics, but he came to disavow some of the philosophical implications of the theory.

"God casts the die, not the dice."
- *Albert Einstein*

This is also translated as "God does not play dice with the universe." But, as a wag has noted (a wag whose name escapes me) not only does God play dice with the universe, s/he throws the dice where you cannot see them.

It's a cool universe we live in. I hope you enjoy the rest of your sojourn in it.

Go in peace.

Quantum Mechanics

Waves are particles.
Particles are waves.
Deal with it.

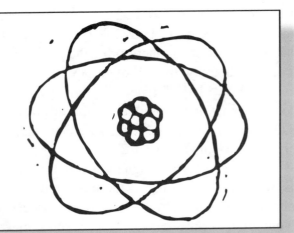

Opening Remarks

"Anyone who is not shocked by quantum theory has not understood it."

- Neils Bohr

Bohr was one of the developers of quantum theory, but that didn't stop him from being upset by it. And it is, really, upsetting. Nothing seems to have the comfortable determinacy of Newtonian mechanics—or even the mathematical certainty of Maxwell's equations. Waves are particles, particles are waves, you can't know where something is if you know where it is going, and particles can destructively interfere with each other....

Wacky stuff. But useful. Quantum theory underlies the technology that I am using to write this—and, if you are in a room with fluorescent lighting, the light that you are reading by. Newton's laws were the ones that were used to put a person on the moon—but quantum mechanics was needed to develop the technology that made it possible.

But even if it is useful, that doesn't mean we have to like it.

"If we are going to stick to the damned quantum jumping, then I regret that I ever had anything to do with quantum theory."

- Erwin Schrödinger, developer of the eponymous equation that is the foundation of one formulation of quantum mechanics.

Necessary Theory

Light as a Particle

Light can be thought of as consisting of photons, "packets" of energy, which are quantized, and have energies given by the following equation:

$E=hf$

In a light emitting diode (LED) photons of light are produced by electrons making energy level transitions. We won't worry too much about the details of how this works, but note the relationships illustrated in Figure 2. An electron, making the rounds of the circuit, is given an energy of 2.0 electron volts by the power supply—as the power supply is putting out a voltage of 2.0 volts. As the electron travels through the circuit, it loses this energy in the LED. The energy is given off in the form of a single photon—which will have an energy that is equal to the energy lost by the electron. (Note: the actual picture is a bit more messy than this; the photon energy can vary a bit from that of the electron because of the band structure of the semiconductor layers in the LED. The energy levels in semiconductors are wide bands. An electron can fall from the top of one band to the bottom of another, making for some variability. We will get a chance to look at this.)

In the lab, you will measure the voltage necessary to turn on an LED, and then compare the electron energy to the photon energy produced.

Figure 1: This quote from Einstein is also translated as "God casts the die, not the dice." Even Einstein, one of the early architects of quantum mechanics and arguably the most brilliant scientist of the 20th century was bothered by quantum mechanics—specifically by some of the philosophical implications. Quantum mechanics has, at its root, an unavoidable degree of randomness. Quantum processes are unpredictable—and unknowable. Einstein wanted to believe that there were certain "hidden variables" that, if known, would render quantum mechanics as deterministic as Newtonian mechanics. In the final decade of the 20th century, experiments were done that suggested fairly convincingly that there could not be such hidden variables—and that quantum theory is, unavoidably, random and unpredictable.

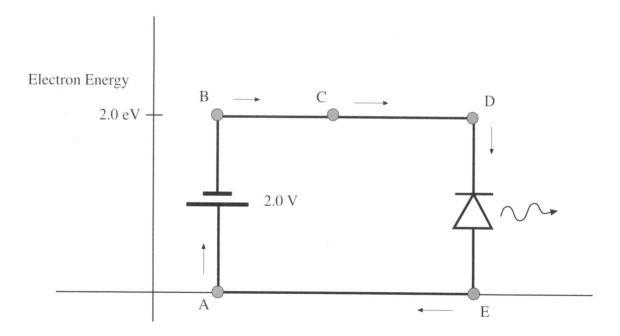

Figure 2: In the above diagram, as the electron moves from point A to point B, it gains an energy of 2.0 eV. (Note: the diagram appears backwards from the usual conventions, as it is designed to show electron current and electron energies—which are backwards from conventional current.) It keeps this energy as it moves from B to C and then from C to D, then loses it as it goes from D to E. The energy is released in the form of a photon.

Particles as Waves

If light, which we are accustomed to thinking of as a wave, can be thought of as a particle, isn't it fair that electrons and other particles can also be thought of as waves? In quantum theory, this is exactly how they are considered: an electron, say, is described by its wave function. And so an electron can behave as a wave: it can diffract, experience interference—and some other things even odder, as we will see.

The basic quantity that one needs to know about a wave is its wavelength; material particles have a deBroglie wavelength associated with them as follows:

$$m= \frac{h}{p} = \frac{h}{mv}$$

In the "Diffraction Suite" simulation, you will consider the patterns that result from the diffraction of particles through double slits. This is a real experiment that can be performed; the net result is a pattern that looks like you would expect for light—with the wavelength given by the above expression.

Experiments and Calculations

Philosophical Note

In what follows, there are a number of things for you to work with, equipment and simulations. But the lab has a different feel than other labs that you have done, as a lot of what you will be doing is just doing something and noting what happens. It would be easy to just do what you are told to do and then just go on. This would be, of course, the easy road. But you will, of course, want more. As you do the different parts, observe what you are asked to observe, but do some reflection: why is this interesting? What does it teach you? Why is it surprising? Give each piece some thought before going on.

Equipment Needed

Each lab group will receive:

> Box with four different colored LEDs
> Variable power supply

In addition, each computer will be loaded with the following simulations, from the Visual Quantum Mechanics project at Kansas State University:

> Spectroscopy
> Diffraction Suite
> Energy Diagram Explorer
> Quantum Tunneling

Each of these simulations is limited in some way, and the actual experiments that they represent would be fiendishly hard to do. But they do allow you to set up initial conditions, and then the situation will evolve according to the Schrödinger equation and the other basic rules of quantum mechanics.

Photon Energies: Simulation I

The fact that electrically gases have a line spectrum was one of the key puzzling experimental facts that was well explained by quantum mechanics. If you think of atoms as having discrete, quantized energy levels, you can imagine that the light which is emitted when electrons make transitions will have certain discrete values.

The "Spectroscopy" program will allow you to explore how the band structure of atomic energy states leads to a discrete line spectrum of gases. Launch the "Spectroscopy" program, and, from the menu of choices presented, under the "Gas Lamps" column, choose the "Emission" option. You will get a screen similar to that in Figure 3. Please proceed as follows:

EXPERIMENT

You will have a selection of lamps that you can use for this experiment. Choose the top one—hydrogen—and drag it to the "socket". Once in the socket, the lamp will light, and

Figure 3: The "Spectroscopy" simulation contains this simulation of the emission from excited gas atoms. By adjusting energy levels and transitions, you can attempt to duplicate the emission spectrum. Note that clicking and dragging on the left side of an energy level will adjust its position; clicking and dragging on the right side will make a transition.

Figure 4: The "Spectroscopy" simulation contains this simulation of the emission from an LED.. Note that the energy levels are now energy bands—a range of energies is possible. This means that a range of wavelengths is emitted.

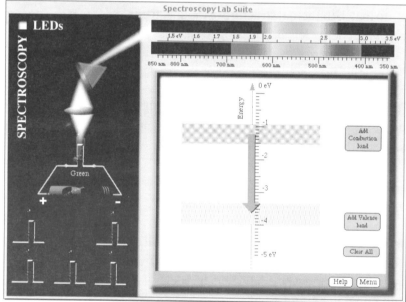

Figure 5: The "Diffraction" program lets you choose different sources of particles, and lets you observe the resulting diffraction patterns when the particles pass through a double slit. You can click on the pattern and use the resulting "grasping hand" to drag a pattern to the storage area to the right for later inspection.

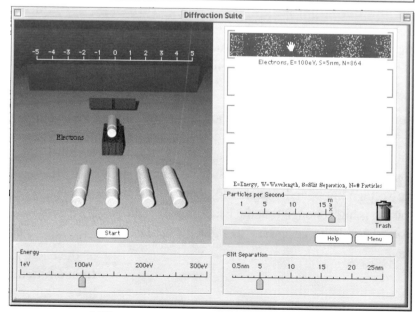

171

you will see a spectrum appear in the top right of the window.

Add an energy level to the system by clicking on the "Add Energy Level" button. Now add another. Drag this energy level to a new location by moving the mouse to the left end of the red line representing the energy level and dragging it up or down. Now move the mouse to the left side of top energy level of the two you have created, and click and drag to the other energy level—you have made a transition.

Add energy levels and transitions and adjust them until the spectrum you create matches the spectrum of the gas. As you do this, try to match the actual structure of the spectrum of the energy levels in hydrogen gas. Review how the energy levels look, either by looking at your class notes or the text.

The emitted light only has certain wavelengths as the atom only has certain energy levels—as you have seen in class.

Photon Energies: Experiment

Before you do another simulation, you will have a chance to work with some real physical equipment—so that the whole lab won't be spent working with computer simulations.

Get the power supply and the LED box, and, noting the cautions that your instructor will explain to you for working with the equipment, proceed as follows:

Connect up the red LED to your power supply. Your power supply will be current limited so that it can't put out enough current to damage the LED—so don't adjust the current knob! But you can adjust the voltage knob, and you should do so—until the voltage is high enough that the LED glows brightly. Note the voltage necessary to light the LED this way.

CALCULATION

The energy from the electrons goes into the energy of the photons. Note the energy that the photons should have, and compute what wavelength and frequency this would give them. Compare this value with a table or chart for values of wavelengths of different colors of light. Does the computed wavelength fall in the red region of the spectrum?

You will have noticed that there are four different colors of LED in the box. And you might well guess that these four different kinds of LED would take four different voltages to run them. You would, in fact, be correct. (It's a bit more complicated than it might seem at first blush, though, as an LED's active element actually emits a range of wavelengths. You can get different color LEDs by simply filtering the resulting light. But, generally, there are differences in the LEDs that we have: different colors will correspond to different transition energies.)

Before you hook up any of the other LEDs in your box, make a prediction:

PREDICTION

For the four different LEDs in your box, rank them in order of the voltage necessary to light them. Which will take the most voltage? Which will take the least?

Once you have made a prediction, test it: hook up your power supply, and note the voltages necessary to light the various LEDs. Note any discrepancies from your prediction, and explain why you might see a difference from what you predicted.

Simulation: Energy Levels in the LED

The energy levels in an LED aren't quite as simple as the energy levels in an atom, so the spectrum of light emitted by an LED isn't a single color: it will have a range of wavelengths. The "Spectroscopy"

172

program you worked with before has an "LED" option that will allow us to explore this.

Start the "Spectroscopy" program (or if you are still running it, click on the "menu" button to get the menu of possibilities back) and choose the "LED" option under the "Solids" column. You will get a screen like that in Figure 4.

 **EXPERIMENT**

Choose a color of LED, and drag it to the socket. The LED will now "light." You will see a spectrum of the LED as well, on the top right.

Add a valence band and a conduction band to the system by clicking on the appropriate buttons. These bands are made up of many, many closely spaced energy levels; all of these may be occupied by electrons. An electron falls from an occupied state in the conduction band into an unoccupied state in the valence band—emitting a photon in the process.

Adjust the spacing of the valence and conduction bands and top and bottom of these bands until the predicted spectrum matches the observed.

? QUESTION ?

Explain why having an energy band—as opposed to a single level—leads to a range of wavelengths in the output.

 **EXPERIMENT**

Now choose a different color of LED, and drag it to the socket. The LED will now "light.", as before.

Add a valence band and a conduction band to the system by clicking on the appropriate buttons. Adjust the spacing of the valence and conduction bands and top and bottom of these bands until the predicted spectrum

matches the observed.

? QUESTION ?

How does this situation differ from the previous situation? Look at the band gap, the color, and the width of the spectrum. Explain any differences that you observe.

Simulation: Diffraction of Particles

In the "Diffraction of Light" lab you had a chance to look at the interference pattern that resulted from the diffraction of light through a double slit. This simulation will deal with the diffraction of matter waves (wave functions) of particles through a double slit. Note that you can really set up an experiment like this, though it is pretty hard to do. And the results that you see from the real experiment are exactly what you will see in the simulation—which makes sense, as the simulation follows the rules of quantum theory.

Start the "Diffraction Suite" simulation. Choose the "Double Slit" option. You will be presented with a screen as in Figure 5. Move the mouse around to see what different things you can control; you can choose different particle sources, adjust the energy of the particles, change the slit separation, and change the number of particles being emitted per unit time.

For starters, choose the "proton" source; this is the one second from the left. Place it in the stand, set the energy to 100 eV, set the particles per second to "Max" and set the slit spacing to 0.2 nm. (Note: some of these may be the default settings and may not need to be changed.) Click the button to run the simulation, and let the data collect for a while until you build up a decent pattern, then stop the simulation. If you move your mouse pointer over the pattern that results, it will turn to a little grasping hand that you can use to grab the pattern and set it in the window on the right in order to save it for later comparison. Do this; set the pattern aside so that you can compare later patterns to it.

Suppose you change something about the slits. You

173

know about diffraction; you should be able to predict how this will affect the resulting pattern.

Change the slit spacing to 0.1 nm. The pattern that you observe on the screen is a diffraction pattern. How will this pattern change if the slit spacing is changed as noted? Think about what you know about diffraction, and make a prediction.

Once you have made a prediction, test it: run the simulation and drag the resulting pattern to your results window where you can compare it to the initial case. Explain any difference between what you predicted and what you observed.

Suppose you were to change something about the particles... how would this affect things?

Keep the proton source in place, but adjust the energy of the protons. Set the energy to 200 eV. Predict what effect this change will make on the observed diffraction pattern. Will the orders be more closely spaced? Less closely spaced?

Once you have made a prediction, test it: run the simulation and drag the resulting pattern to your results window where you can compare it to the initial case. Explain any difference between the two patterns, and any difference between what you predicted and what you observed.

Now, suppose you chose a different source of particles... how would this affect things?

Choose the "pion" source, which is at the far right. Pions are hadrons like protons, but are lighter—about 1/7 the mass of the proton. Set the energy to 100 eV, the particles per

second to "Max" and the slit spacing to 0.2 nm. When you run the simulation, how will the pattern differ: will the spacing between "light" areas (where more particles have hit) be greater or less than before? Think: the wavelength depends on the momentum, which depends on the mass and velocity. But you have fixed the particles' energy, not the momentum! Will a lighter particle with the same energy have more or less momentum? How will this affect the wavelength? And how will this affect the resulting interference pattern? There are many steps here! Think them through, and outline your thought process.

Once you have made a prediction, test it: run the simulation and drag the resulting pattern to your results window where you can compare it to the initial case. Explain any difference between the two patterns, and any difference between what you predicted and what you observed.

More on Diffraction

Now it is time to look at the wackiest thing about diffraction. It's real, too: you can set up an experiment just like the simulation that you will do that gives exactly the same results.

Choose the "electron" source (the one on the far left) and set the energy to 100 eV, the slit spacing to 5 nm, and the particles per second to "Max." Now, click to run the simulation, and let enough particles build up to make a good pattern. Use the little grasping hand to set the pattern aside for later comparison.

Next, set the particles per second to 5. If there are only 5 particles per second, given how fast the particles move, there will only be one electron in the picture at any one time. Let a good pattern build up; it will take longer than before. But note this: how does the pattern appear compared to the one you saw before? If you let it get as dark, you should note that it appears about the same. Check it an see!

The key result is this: the pattern is a result of diffraction and interference. We have seen this before with light waves. This is a diffraction pattern that appears from matter waves. But note: you just ran the experiment with one particle at a time. So any diffraction pattern that appears is due to a diffraction and interference of a particle with... *itself!* The wave function diffracts through both slits, and subsequently interferes with itself. Which leads to the following question....

? QUESTION ?

Which of the two slits did the particle go through? Think about it—and ask your instructor for hints and clarification.

This is one of the oddest results of quantum theory: a sort of non-locality. And you can do a real experiment that shows that the world really does seem to work this way.

Weird.

Bound States

Next, we will look at a classical situation that has an interesting quantum analog.

Start the "Energy Diagram Explorer" program; the opening screen looks like this:

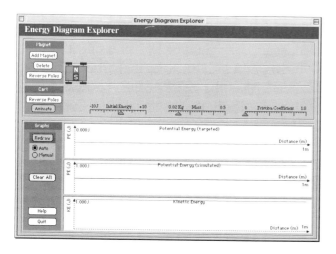

You can play with several different controls on this one. There is a little cart with a magnet on it that will be the subject of our investigations; click on "Animate" and it will roll back and forth. Cool,

isn't it? Now, let's build a "potential well" for the cart. Click on the "Add Magnet" button, and drag the added magnet over to the right side. Click on the "Add Magnet" button again, and drag the added magnet just a tad to the right. Now drag the little cart to the middle of the screen. If the magnets in this case were drawn right—and they don't seem to be—the magnets would repel the magnet on the cart, and push it back toward the center. Of course, if the cart is moving, it might have enough energy to overcome this repulsion.... Use the "Initial Energy" slider to set the initial energy to 4 J—you can note on the graph that this makes the kinetic energy just a tad less than the potential energies of the peaks—and so the energy is just a bit less than what is needed to overcome the repulsion of the magnets. You should end up with a situation that looks like this:

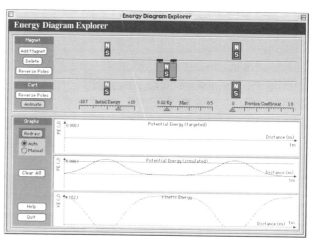

Now, animate it, and watch what happens. Yep, the cart rolls back and forth. This is what we call a bound state—with the cart trapped in what we call a potential well.

Now, adjust the energy so that the cart's energy is higher than the energy of the barriers that keep it in place. What does the cart do now, when you animate the situation?

We will see quantum cases that look like this too: a particle constrained by a potential barrier. When we look at the quantum cases, you might find it useful to think about this classical case to help you get a handle on what is going on.

But there are a couple of big differences between

the classical and quantum case...

i) Where the cart spends its time. Where the cart is likely to be found is a bit different in the quantum case.

ii) Whether the cart can escape or not.

With the energy level of the cart set lower than the energy of the barrier, the cart will bounce back and forth forever—and will never escape. It won't escape unless the energy is high enough—as you saw. If the energy is too low, it stays put. If it is high enough, the cart escapes.

But the quantum case is different....

Tunnelling

Next, start the "Quantum Tunnelling" simulation. In this case, there is a wave function, perhaps for an electron or some other particle, and a barrier—like the barriers in the last simulation. Keep the defaults that the program starts with. You will get a screen like this:

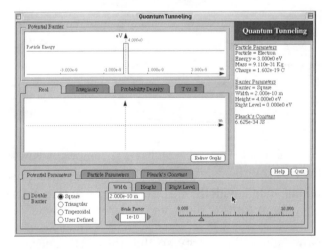

Note the flashing button that says, "Redraw Graphs." It is fairly begging for you to click it, isn't it? In this case, do not resist temptation. Click it. And note the wave function that results.

The wave function initially started on the left side. But, as you will note, a bit of it has "tunneled" to the right side of the barrier! Note: there are tabs labelled "Real", "Imaginary", "Probability Density" and "T vs. E". (Technical note: a wave function

is a complex function, with real and imaginary parts. (In this way, I suppose, it's a lot like my life: complex, with real and imaginary parts.) You can look at either part, or the probability density, which depends on both. The probability density is what is real, in the sense that you usually use this word.) We will generally use the "Real" tab or the "Probability Density" tab—which shows the probability of finding the particle. If you click on the "Probability Density" tab, you can see there is a certain probability to find the particle on the other side of the barrier.... Where, classically, it should never be found.

Weird. But real. We have devices in our labs that rely on this tunneling through an energetically forbidden zone for their operation.

 **EXPERIMENT**

Change the width of the barrier, using the slider at the bottom right. Choose "Potential Parameters" and choose "Width" and make the barrier wider. How does this affect how much tunneling occurs? Comment. Now make the barrier very thin. How does this affect how much tunnelling occurs? Comment.

 **EXPERIMENT**

Now reset to the initial conditions. Adjust the barrier height, first by increasing it and then by decreasing it. Keep the barrier height greater than the energy of the particle, so that, classically, the particle should never be able to make it through the barrier.

There's a flip side to tunneling which is interesting as well....

 **EXPERIMENT**

Set the energy level of the barrier to a value that is less than the energy of the particle—the barrier height will be lower than the red line that denotes the particle

176

energy. (You can do this by choosing the "Potential Parameters" tab, choosing the "Height" tab, and using the slider.) Redraw the graph, click on the "Real" tab to look at the real part of the wave function. What do you note? The barrier is so small that the particle should cruise right on by with nary a whimper. But does it? Comment.

It makes sense, I suppose, that if a particle can tunnel through a barrier that it doesn't have enough energy to surmount that it should bounce off a barrier that it should easily clear. Nature is perverse in this case, but in a fair-minded way.

Summing Up

One of the side effects of particles being represented as wave functions is that particles have to follow wave rules. One of these is uncertainty. Where is a wave? It is not really localized; it is distributed in some sense. If you make a really skinny wave, so you know where it is, it will spread out quickly—after some time, it won't be localized any more. In essence, you won't know where it is going.

This particular nugget of quantum wisdom is enshrined as Heisenberg's Uncertainty Principle. It states that it is not possible to know, precisely, both a particle's position and its momentum. You can know where it is, or know where it is going—but not both. So: if you know where you are, can you know where you are going?

> A quantum mechanic's vacation
> Had her colleagues in dire consternation
> For while studies had shown
> That her speed was well known
> Her position was pure speculation

Quantum rules certainly govern how our bodies behave at an atomic level, but considered as a whole, your body is a large enough entity that quantum rules really don't apply. The uncertainty principle limits my ability to locate, say, my golden retriever—quantum mechanics says that there will always be some uncertainty in where she is. Given her size and speed, this uncertainty is many, many orders of magnitude less than the size of the nucleus of an atom, so, in practice, this is not a significant limitation. And if she can't find a tennis ball I throw, she can't claim it is because of the uncertainty principle either.

Go in peace.

Figure 6: One of the best ways to show the essential weirdness of the quantum world is by a thought experiment (or "gedanken" experiment) called "Schrödinger's Cat." In this thought experiment, a cat is placed inside a box with a container of poisonous gas, which will be released if a particle of radioactive material in a trigger mechanism decays. The cat is in the box for exactly one half-life. At the end of this time, the particle has a 50% chance of having decayed. But you could argue that since the box is closed, we haven't been able to observe if that atom decays or not. In quantum terms, the atom will be in a mixed state: 50% decayed, and 50% undecayed. Does this then mean that the cat is in a mixed state—50% dead and 50% alive? We will talk about this in class.

Radon

A Radioactive Gas and its Troublesome Offspring

Opening Remarks

In the 1500's it became apparent that there were certain mines in Europe - notably the Joachimistal and Schneeberg mines in the Erz Mountains - in which miners tended to suffer untimely and mysterious deaths from what was called *Bergkrankheit* (mountain sickness.)[1] But it was not until 1926 - and after the deaths of presumably thousands of miners - that authorities admitted that about *half* of the miners in the Joachimistal mines were succumbing to lung cancer. Later research revealed the cause, which could not have been known until this century: extremely high levels of radon gas, a by-product of the natural radioactive disintegration of uranium.

When the uranium that is reasonably ubiquitous in the earth's crust decays, it produces a long series of further decays. This sequence is illustrated in Figure 2. There are two especially notable decay products being formed: radium (Ra), a metal, and radon (Rn), which is a noble gas. Radium, having the short half-life that it does, is very radioactive. One gram of radium will experience 37,000,000,000 disintegrations per second - in short, a lot - and in the process gives off so much ionizing radiation that it will ionize the air around it and will actually glow, a fact that delighted the discoverer of radium, Marie Curie.

"Don't light the lamps," Marie said in the darkness. Then she added with a little laugh: "Do you remember the day when you said to me 'I should like radium to have a beautiful color?'"

Marie Curie to husband Pierre. Eve Curie, from *Madame Curie*, a biography of her mother

Radium, being so intensely radioactive (which is why it was named what it was), was used almost immediately in legitimate medical treatments for cancer and other ailments. And it caught the public fancy; it was associated with healing, and so was a good thing, and it was an emblem of the excitement of scientific discovery of the times. A new element had been discovered that exhibited - to an extreme degree - a newly discovered property of matter. And so radium - and the name - were used for a wide variety of things, some legitimate, but most not. Given the novelty and the cachet, folks worried less about being exposed to radiation. Orange pottery from earlier parts of this century was often colored with uranium oxide, which gives it a nice orange color - and makes it quite radioactive. One Fiestaware chop plate that I found in an antique store I estimated to be more radioactive than all of the sources in our Modern Physics lab put together. (Granted, we don't have very many - or very intense - sources, but I was surprised to find something this hot just sitting on a shelf with no warning label!)

Something that was discovered very soon after the discovery of radium was that it gave off an *emanation* that was also radioactive. This is the gas we now know as radon: a noble gas with a very short half-life. What is important about radon is this: as a noble gas, it doesn't form chemical compounds lightly. So, when the uranium in the rocks and soil under your house decays (there is uranium in the rocks and soil under your house, but probably not a lot) it produces radium, which stays put, and then radon - which does not. The radon will percolate up from the ground. And, like as not, it will end up in your basement.

This is really not so bad. You can breathe in radon in reasonable concentrations with no ill effects; the radon is a noble gas, and so won't stick around in your body

Figure 1: Did these matches really have radium in them? I don't think so. But the box caught my eye when I found it in an antique shop recently. In the early part of this century, radiation was not something to be avoided or minimized - it was something to be embraced. Radium, in particular, had a certain cachet. In another shop I found a device called the "Revigator" that was sold to add radioactivity in the form of radon to drinking water. It was said to contain radium ore, which really meant that it contained uranium ore, which produces radium as part of its decay chain. There is a certain style of depression glass which was said to have a "radium finish," even though there is no radium in the finish. Generally, folks thought that radium was pretty cool stuff. A lot of why this is true has to do with legitimate uses of radium in the health professions; it was used to treat - effectively - a wide range of diseases. But radium - and radon - are not, generally, good for your health. After World War II, when the consequences of exposure to radiation became more clear, the public perception of radiation changed. But it is not possible to avoid radioactivity; a certain amount is natural. It is in the environment, and a certain amount is in your body!

long enough to cause too much trouble. But the radon gas molecules in the air will decay to a series of very short-lived isotopes of various metals. These will stick to things like dust particles in the air, and these dust particles will stick to things - like your lung tissue. And so the radon *progeny*, as these atoms are known, are worth worrying about. And where there is radon, there are radon progeny.

It turns out that it is not hard to catch these radon progeny for study. You can just suck a lot of air through a filter, and the dust with the radon progeny will stick to it. Recently, I stuck a filter on the input of a blower from the labs, ran it for ten minutes in the basement of the Weber building, and stuck it up next to a Geiger counter. I was measuring 500 counts per minute from

the dust on the filter - compared to about 50 counts per minute from background radiation. But the count rate decreased; after a few days, the filter had no observable radioactivity. The isotopes from the radon decay have short half-lives, and do go away.

In this lab, you will have a chance to perform a similar experiment yourself, as well as make measurements on some other radioactive sources.

Necessary Theory

Radioactive Decay

We are assuming that you have a good grounding

in the basics of radioactive decay: that atoms decay by emitting alpha particles (helium nuclei, two protons and two neutrons) and beta particles (electrons) at high speeds, or the high energy photons called gamma rays. We don't observe the decay; we merely see the product of the decay, the high-energy particle or photon that is given off in the decay. This is detected by a Geiger Counter; for an explanation of this device, see the lab on it.

Shielding

Given that the alphas, betas and gammas emitted by radioactive substances are injurious to the tissues in your body, it is worthwhile to know a bit about them. They do their damage by ionizing atoms that they pass; as the charged alpha and beta particles go through matter, they ionize atoms along their path. If the atoms are ones that are crucial to the operation of a cell in your body, the cell may die. The cells in your body that are most susceptible to radiation damage are those cells that are reproducing most rapidly: cells in your bone marrow and the lining of your digestive tract. Gamma rays are somewhat different; they tend to have an all-or-nothing interaction with atoms: they will penetrate matter to a certain depth and then knock an electron off an atom so hard that it creates its own ionization trail. Gamma rays are more penetrating than alphas and betas, and so are harder to shield against. Alpha particles leave a big, fat ionization trail, and so do a lot more damage than betas or gammas, but they are less penetrating - they give up their energy quickly.

The sources that you will use in the lab today are very safe, as long as you don't eat them. They can be easily and effectively shielded, and, in the case of the dust, will become harmless quite quickly.

Counting Statistics

Radioactive decays are random events. We measure radioactivity by measuring the decays of individual atoms with a Geiger counter or other instrument. If you have a certain number of atoms, each one has a certain chance of decaying in one second - so you will observe a certain number of decays. If you have twice the number of atoms,

you should see about twice as many decays in one second. This means that we can use a measurement of the number of decays per second as a measure of the number of radioactive atoms - with one big caveat.

Since the decays are random, there is a certain amount of fluctuation that will occur. Figure 3 shows data taken with the equipment that you will use for this lab, measuring the number of decays in each second from a slowly-decaying source (an orange plate glazed with uranium oxide) for a period of ten minutes. You can see that the number of decays seen in each second fluctuates - the number observed in one second is as high as 195 and as low as 115. But the values do tend to cluster in the middle of this range, near 155 or so. The second graph is a histogram of the data; the bars show for how many intervals a particular value was recorded. It is clear that the values near the center (which, no surprise, is approximately the average value) are more likely, and the values farther away from the average are less likely. This is a classic normal distribution (well, technically it's really a Poisson distribution, but in this limit it approximates a normal distribution pretty well), with the standard deviation describing the width of the distribution.

For this kind of statistics, the standard deviation can be approximated very simply: if the expected number of counts in an interval is N, the expected standard deviation is $\sqrt{N}$. So we can take as an estimate of the number of counts in some interval, including error:

$$Counts = N \pm \sqrt{N}$$

The more you count, the more the error - but the relative error is less. The error, as a fraction of the number of counts, is given by:

$$Error = \frac{1}{\sqrt{N}}$$

For example, if you measure 100 counts, the expected error is ±10, which is 10%. If you measure 10,000 counts, the expected error is ±100, which is 1%.

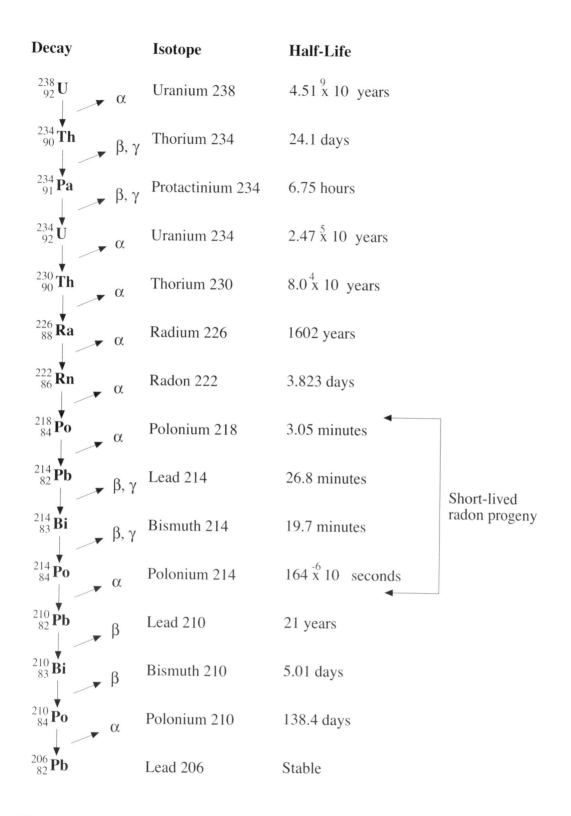

Decay	Isotope	Half-Life
$^{238}_{92}\text{U}$ → α	Uranium 238	4.51×10^{9} years
$^{234}_{90}\text{Th}$ → β, γ	Thorium 234	24.1 days
$^{234}_{91}\text{Pa}$ → β, γ	Protactinium 234	6.75 hours
$^{234}_{92}\text{U}$ → α	Uranium 234	2.47×10^{5} years
$^{230}_{90}\text{Th}$ → α	Thorium 230	8.0×10^{4} years
$^{226}_{88}\text{Ra}$ → α	Radium 226	1602 years
$^{222}_{86}\text{Rn}$ → α	Radon 222	3.823 days
$^{218}_{84}\text{Po}$ → α	Polonium 218	3.05 minutes
$^{214}_{82}\text{Pb}$ → β, γ	Lead 214	26.8 minutes
$^{214}_{83}\text{Bi}$ → β, γ	Bismuth 214	19.7 minutes
$^{214}_{84}\text{Po}$ → α	Polonium 214	164×10^{-6} seconds
$^{210}_{82}\text{Pb}$ → β	Lead 210	21 years
$^{210}_{83}\text{Bi}$ → β	Bismuth 210	5.01 days
$^{210}_{84}\text{Po}$ → α	Polonium 210	138.4 days
$^{206}_{82}\text{Pb}$	Lead 206	Stable

Short-lived radon progeny

Figure 2: Uranium 238, which occurs with a reasonable abundance in the earth's crust, goes through a long chain of alpha, beta and gamma decays before becoming stable lead 206. Along the way, a uranium atom will decay to radon - a noble gas - which decays to a series of short-lived progeny. These species are very radioactive, due to their short half-lives, and will collect on dust in the air.

In this lab, you will make measurements of radioactive decays of a dust sample. You will be using the number of decays observed as a measure of the number of radioactive atoms present. The longer you count, the more accurately you can estimate how many atoms are really there, but there is a fly in the ointment: since your sample is made up of atoms with short half-lives, the number of atoms will be changing! So the longer you count, in some sense the *worse* your estimate would be. Oh well; no one said it would be easy.

Experiments and Calculations

Equipment Needed

Each group will be provided with the following equipment:

> Geiger Counter (actual tube is on back; note window)
> ULI interface and Macintosh computer
> Event Counter software
> Uranium orange plate or other crockery (get when needed only)
> Air source and filter for dust collection

There are two main points to be aware of:

• The plates are not very easy to find these days (at least at the prices that we want to pay for them, which is not much) and are fragile; please be careful with them! I comb the flea markets looking for them, but even I have only so much tolerance for this sort of thing.

• Get the orange plate only when you need it. Don't pick it up until you are ready for the part of the lab that uses it, and put it back when you are finished with it.

• The air source that you will use to collect dust is quite noisy; be sure that you put it somewhere that it does not bother people.

Background

There is a certain amount of radiation that you are exposed to all the time regardless of whether you have an orange plate near you or not. There are cosmic rays from space, radiation from radon in the air, radiation from the ground, and even a small amount of radiation from folks around you (your body contains some amount of radioactivity, mostly in the form of potassium isotopes.) It is worth measuring this value.

Set your detector on the table, well away from any radiation sources. Set the count interval to 5 minutes, and the run time to 10 minutes. Start counting, and note the first number as it comes in. After you get a number, compute its uncertainty. Next, compute a background radiation level, and its uncertainty, in counts per minute. When the second number comes in, note: does this value for the background agree with the first number, within uncertainty?

Think about the size of the detector in your Geiger tube, which you can see on the back of your counter unit. It's pretty small. You, being much larger, will be hit by a much larger number of particles. There is a significant amount of radiation that you are exposed to naturally. It is worthwhile to know that we get a significant amount more background radiation than other folks in the country because of the composition of our soil and our altitude. We see about three times as much cosmic radiation as do folks living at sea level, and our soil has a fair amount of uranium in it. There are other natural sources of radioactivity as well (bananas have some, taking a shower exposes you to some) which I would be happy to talk about if you are interested. None of these sources are really large enough to worry about, but they are interesting to know about.

Radon and Progeny

As discussed in earlier sections. our soils in Colorado contain a fair amount of uranium - which decays to radium, which decays to radon, which will percolate up through the soil into the air. The radon will tend to collect in the basements of buildings where there is not very good air handling and where there is a lot of air infiltration. The basements of old buildings are especially notorious for this. In the following experiment, you will run an air sampler that will pull a significant amount of air

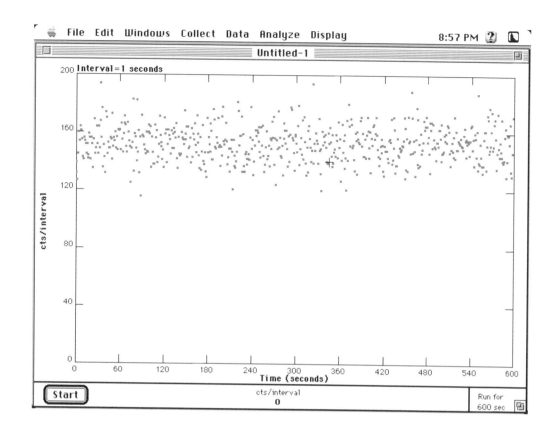

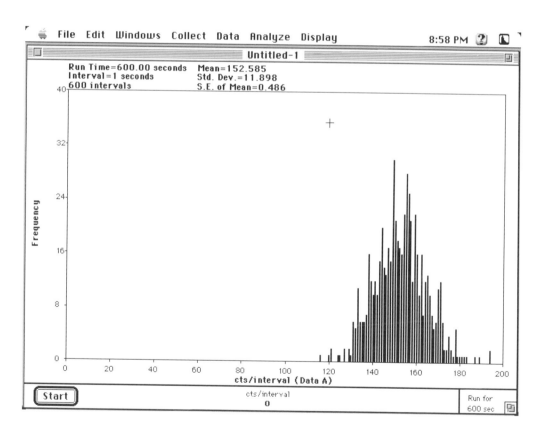

Figure 3: The top graph shows counts per second, measured each second for 600 seconds, from a uranium orange plate. The bottom graph shows a histogram of this data - the number of occurrences of each number of counts for the various intervals.

through a filter. This filter will not trap any radon gas, radon being a noble gas, but it will trap radon progeny: the metal elements that radon decays into. These short-lived isotopes will tend to stick to dust particles in the air, which will be trapped by the filter. If you pull air through a filter and collect dust from the air, it is possible to collect a large sample of a reasonable level of activity.

Your class should discuss, as a group, places on campus where it might be interesting to sample the air to see if there is a fair amount of radon in the air. For this part of the lab, it is best if the different lab groups find different places to sample. You need somewhere that no one will be bothered by the air source, which is quite noisy. It might also be nice to compare outside air with inside air; on some occasions, we have found that we got significant radon levels outdoors, especially near where tunnels come to the surface.

Each group will have an air source that can be used to sample air. Pick a spot on campus where you would like to sample the air, and run the source for about 10 minutes with a filter on the front to collect a dust sample.

Next, you will need to collect some data on the radiation in your sample. You will be measuring the count rate from the sample vs. time. Set your count interval to one minute, and the run time to 60 minutes. Fold up your filter so that it will fit underneath the tube in your counter, set the counter on top of the filter, and start counting.

Let the unit collect data for a few minutes. Once you have recorded a few minutes worth of data, compute the observed radiation level in counts per minute for your sample, with an uncertainty estimate. Does the radiation level that you observe differ significantly from background? Inform your instructor of the radiation level that you note as well as where your sample was from. After all of the groups have reported values, your instructor should lead the class in a discussion of what values were obtained for air sampled in different places around campus.

QUESTION

Where are the radiation levels high? Where are they low? Does this make sense in terms of what you know about how radon gets into buildings? (Note: we also see great seasonal differences. If you are doing this lab in the spring, you are apt to find much lower radiation levels than in the winter. Why would this be?

Let your unit keep taking data for a long enough time that you can see a definite decay in the radiation rate.

Radioactive Decay

As noted, you should let your unit keep collecting data. Watch the data as it is collected; is the count rate changing? Why is it changing? If you see a significant change, can you estimate a half-life for your sample? Does this make sense in terms of the half-lives of the various atoms that are likely to be on the filter? The half-life for this sample is a complicated business to predict. One atom decays into another decays into another - with a count at each step of the way. But at some point, the atoms will decay away. Lead 214 atoms have a half-life of 26.8 minutes. But each atom that decays makes an atom of Bismuth 214 - which has a half-life of 19.7 minutes! So you aren't getting rid of radioactive atoms right away. Nonetheless, you should find that the half-life you see is in line with the half-lives of the various atoms. A half-life of 2 hours would be surprising, as would one of 2 minutes.

You may well find that you don't have a high enough count rate to see any change with time. You should look at the data that other groups are compiling. For groups who are measuring large count rates, do you see the count rate decreasing with time?

If you have enough data to estimate a half-life, be sure to take into account background! You are not interested in knowing when the count rate has decreased by half, but when the portion of the count rate that can be ascribed to the radioactive source has decreased by half. You will need to subtract off the background. And don't forget about error!

Counting Statistics

Get an orange plate as a source, and set your Geiger counter on top of it. Set the count interval to one second (under the "Collect" menu) and the run time to sixty seconds (again, under the "Collect" menu.) Turn the Geiger counter on (just use the "On" setting, not the "Audio" setting; this is unconscionably annoying) and take some data.

QUESTION

You will have taken sixty measurements of the counts per second. Get the statistics on your data by choosing the "Stats" option under the "Analyze" menu. Note the mean and the standard deviation. Given the measured value of the mean, does the standard deviation have about the value that you would predict?

Radioactive decay is a random process - and is governed by the laws of probability in this regard. There is no way to predict when a particular atom will decay - and so the count rate from a source will have a certain scatter to it, as you have seen.

Distance and Shielding

There are two ways to reduce the amount of radiation you receive from a radioactive source: distance, and shielding. The further away you are from a radioactive source, the less radiation you will see from it. And the more material you put between you and the source, the less radiation you will see.

Set your count interval to one minute, and the run time to ten minutes. Take your orange plate and set it very close to your detector. Start counting. As soon as the first count comes in, quickly move the plate a little bit farther away from the detector. When this count comes in, move the plate a little bit farther away - and so on. Do ten minutes worth of measurements, each time moving the plate a bit farther away from your detector. Does the trend in the data appear as you would expect? About how

far away from the detector would the plate have to be in order to have the measured count rate be indistinguishable from background? (You will need to consider uncertainty here.)

Next, let's look at shielding. Use your lab manual as a source of shielding: one page, two pages, and so on. As before, set your count interval to one minute, but this time set the run time to twenty minutes. Set your detector directly on your orange plate. Start counting. When the first count comes in, immediately note the number and put one page of the lab manual between the plate and the detector. When the second count comes in, put one more page of the lab manual (for a total of two) between the plate and the detector. Keep doing this, adding an additional page of shielding every minute. The net result will be a graph of the counts per minute as a function of time in minutes - or pages of shielding. Take a look at the graph; what trends do you see? Note that there are different kinds of radiation that come from the plate: alpha particles, which take very little shielding to stop, beta particles, which take more shielding to stop, and gamma rays, which are quite penetrating. Can you tell this from the graph of the data you have just obtained? Can you see a "signature" of different kinds of radiation? (For instance: if one piece of paper dramatically drops the count rate, and the second drops it only a small amount, this could mean that the first piece of paper stops the alphas, but the second sheet doesn't stop all of the betas or gammas.)

QUESTION

How much shielding does it take to reduce the radiation to essentially background levels? If the number of pages you have used in the previous experiment was not sufficient, do a quick experiment to determine how much shielding would be necessary to reduce the radiation by the necessary amount. This is a very practical detail...

QUESTION

My wife is a Fiestaware fanatic, though she does not collect orange. If she did, and she kept an orange plate in a closed cabinet in our kitchen, would I have cause to be worried about the radiation?

Summing Up

"Dusty, I've found over my lifetime the secret to staying calm in a crisis is not to have all the facts."

- Lefty, from "The Lives of the Cowboys", on *Prairie Home Companion,* a radio program by Garrison Keillor

Radiation is a very scary danger to some people because of its insidious nature: radon gas can't be seen or smelled, it infiltrates your house through your basement, and you could get a dangerous dose of it without even knowing about it. I know many people, who, when asked about the radon levels in their houses, say, "I don't want to know." But ignorance is not a good way to protect yourself, and the reality is really not all that scary. There is radioactivity in the environment, but the chances are very good that you are not being exposed to enough to worry about. And if you are, being exposed to a significant amount of radiation from radon levels in your basement, not knowing about it is not a good form of protection - ventilation is.

Go in peace.

References

1. J. Newell Stannard, *Radioactivity and Health: A History*, US DOE, Office of Health and Environmental Research (1988).

Many folks are worried that their computers are giving off "radiation." In fact, they do give off electromagnetic waves, and perhaps a *very* small amount of x-rays. But computer screens build up a static charge, which makes them attract dust - and this dust, as you have seen, is slightly radioactive. So there is a bit of radiation coming from the computer - but not for the reason most people think!

CSU Physics
Proudly
Presents:

ONE WEEK ONLY!
Little Shop
of Physics

Introduction

By this point in the year, you have done many exciting physics experiments. You are to be commended for the work that you have done.

As our reward to you, we are setting up a special week in the lab. For several years a group of students (mostly Physics majors, but students from other majors have dominated over the past few years) and I have been putting together a collection of hands-on demonstration experiments that illustrate various aspects of physics. We take these experiments all over the region, sharing cool science with kids of all ages. It's pretty neat.

But this is the best week of all in the Little Shop year, when we get to share things with the students at Colorado State. For your enjoyment, we have assembled over 120 experiments, including:

❈ How do you look in uv light? ❈
Worse than you expected, i bet!

Amazing Auditory Illusions
Can you trust your ears?

✳ The Peripatetic Plasma Ball ✳
The very symbol of the
Little Shop of Physics

and a bunch of other experiments too numerous to mention. It's a nice finish to your year of Physics.

Theory

All the theory you will need you already know. What do you think we taught you all that stuff for?

Procedures

i) Come to lab.

ii) Join your lab partners as usual.

iii) Look at all the neat experiments. See if you can figure out what is going on for each of them.

iv) Answer the following questions as you explore. Your answers to these questions will serve as your report.

QUESTION

Can you find one experiment that uses the principle that a magnetic field makes a force on a moving charge? Name the experiment, and explain how it works.

QUESTION

Changing magnetic fields may induce a current flow. Find an experiment that uses this principle and explain how it works.

QUESTION

There are many different kinds of electromagnetic waves. Find two experiments that use electromagnetic waves other than light in a key way, and describe what it is they do.

QUESTION

It is possible to produce a real image by reflection. Can you find an experiment that shows this? Explain what it is you are seeing.

QUESTION

Many times our eyes are not a reliable guide to the world. Give an example of an experiment that shows this, and explain what is going on.

Final Comment

We are always looking for new experiments for the Little Shop. These experiments are on the road to a different school every week; tens of thousands of kids see the equipment we have each year, and so the life expectancy of things is not as long as it could be. A steady supply of new stuff is crucial.

In short, we need your help. We have ideas for good exhibits, and neat stuff, and tools, and money... All we need is your help. You can get one academic credit for developing an exhibit, from one of our ideas or one of yours, and you get to take it along on one of our school visits. This is an especially good opportunity for anyone who might want to teach some day—you get to have some real, hands-on experience in a school setting. The enthusiasm of young children in particular is very inspiring. If this sounds like it might be fun, talk to Brian Jones or Adam Beehler for more details. Heck, if this works out, perhaps you might end up working for the Little Shop. It's a great group of folks, and it makes a heck of a good job.

Thanks for all your good work this semester. We hope that you have learned from and enjoyed your experience in the lab. And, should you want to spread a little of this knowledge and excitement around, you now know where to turn.

Go in peace.

About the Author

Brian Jones (the older of the two people in the above photo) teaches undergraduate courses in the Physics Department, and directs the instructional labs for theDepartment. He is best known as the Director of the Little Shop of Physics, a traveling hands-on science outreach program. He has a Master's degree in Physics from Cornell University, and has also taught at Kenyon College in Gambier, Ohio and at Waterford Kamhlaba United World College in Mbabane, Swaziland.

About the Manual

This manual is meant to be more than a cookbook to follow in lab. The information is meant to give you an introduction and overview to the experiment ("the big picture"), to serve as a practical guide to the use of the equipment, and to give you some ideas as to what measurements to take and what to make of them. Much of what you do, though, will be up to your initiative. This lab will be what you make of it. Ideally, the lab manual should also be used outside of lab. It is designed to be read carefully before lab, chuckled over in quiet moments between classes in the student center, and perhaps discussed with great intensity over cups of espresso. It is most likely not something that you will want to hand down to your children, but it is hopefully something that you will look on at the end of the course and think that you got your money's worth before stuffing it in an attic or turning it in to be recycled.

About the Lab

The goal of this lab course is to create an environment in which students can explore some physics, clarify some of the concepts of the course, and enhance their physical intuition. Such hands-on learning is very important to a full understanding of an empirical science like physics. If you are taking this course, you are most likely preparing for a career in which these skills are essential. The lab, in addition to being useful, is also supposed to be enjoyable. The world we live in is a fascinating place, and learning a bit about its workings can be interesting, exciting and fun.